CW00833172

# Loving Christian

## One family's journey
## through schizophrenia

*To Chrissie v Robin*

*Love Georgie xx*

## Georgina Wakefield

***PCCS BOOKS***
Ross-on-Wye

PCCS BOOKS
2 Cropper Row
Alton Road
Ross-on-Wye
HR9 5LA
UK
Tel +44 (0)1989 763900
www.pccs-books.co.uk


First published in 2010

© Georgina Wakefield, 2010

All rights reserved.
No part of this publication may be reproduced, stored in a retrieval
system, transmitted or utilised in any form by any means, electronic,
mechanical, photocopying or recording or otherwise without permission
in writing from the publishers.


Georgina Wakefield has asserted her rights to be identified as
the author of this work in accordance with the Copyright, Designs
and Patents Act 1988.

**Loving Christian: One family's journey through schizophrenia**

ISBN  978 1 906254 30 8


Cover design in the UK by Old Dog Graphics
Typeset in the UK by The Old Dog's Missus in 'Univers'
Printed in the UK by ImprintDigital.net
Cover photograph © Jamie Hughes

# CONTENTS

## DEDICATION

I dedicate this book to my youngest son Christian John Wakefield who has managed to find the strength to cope with paranoid schizophrenia for 20 years.

# Foreword

## Antony Sheehan

Living independently – a fulfilling and happy life is all that most people ask for. A life of choices and opportunity, a life free of prejudice and discrimination, a life of social participation and well-being. All of us accept the highs and lows, the fact that life is indeed the proverbial roller coaster.

For some of us though and for some members of our families, the experience is a tougher one. For some people with mental health problems, life in 2010 can still be characterised by experiences of exclusion, oppression and prejudice – the manifestation of ignorance. We know all too well the consequences of such experiences, namely lack of opportunity to participate, to have housing of one's own choosing, to have a job and to make friends.

A recent report on Independent Living from Demos[1] suggested that 'we have only just begun on the road to full equality' for people with physical or emotional impairment. The report goes on to say that there are opportunities to bring about greater equality for people with disability to achieve the 'roller-coaster' model of life that many take for granted instead of the social exclusion that significant numbers of our fellow citizens encounter. The next phase of mental health reform has to be about challenging the ignorance and prejudice that confines people to living on the margins.

In writing this book, Georgina Wakefield has provided a wonderful story, a family's story. It is a story of love, of great achievement, as well as difficult challenges. It is a story of mental health and its impact on a family. A frank account of just how much stigma can exacerbate the experience of being mentally ill. The story is a profound one that holds a mirror up to the structures

Antony Sheehan is Chief Executive of Leicestershire Partnership NHS Trust. He was formerly a Director General at the Department of Health.

1. Demos (2005) *Independent Living: The right to be equal.*

of the society in which we live and just how easy it is to be disenfranchised from those structures if one moves away from the usual track of life's ups and downs. The story is also a critique for the mental health system itself. Incisive observations are offered as to what is the very best and worst of the system, telling examples of what needs to be put right in our own 'back yard'. Wakefield makes a plea for greater hope to be offered. I stand by her in making that plea and join with her in asking for recovery to be the theme for mental health care in this country.

It is true that much has been achieved in the first phase of reform of mental health care in England. Since the National Service Framework for Mental Health (NSFMH) was published[2] progress can be summarised as: much greater access to better-organised community services such as assertive outreach, home treatment and early intervention. We have more mental health professionals, more availability of modern medications and genuine reductions in the rate of suicide. In his report on the first five years of delivery of the NSFMH,[3] Louis Appleby refers to a period of unprecedented progress, but he also highlights areas which require action, including better mental health care for people from black and other ethnic minority communities, better access to psychological therapies and acting to reduce the stigma associated with mental illness.

In 2004 a report was published through the combined efforts of the National Institute for Mental Health in England (NIMHE) and the government's Social Exclusion Unit (SEU).[4] The report highlighted the scandal that is the experience of some with mental illness. A picture was painted of poorer opportunity in relation to almost every indicator of social functioning. An action plan was also developed, now being led by NIMHE with cross-government backing, to address some of the main institutional barriers to inclusion.

As well as these specific actions in respect of mental health, more general action across government provides useful opportunities to participate as equal citizens. The work of the Prime Minister's

2. Department of Health (2002) *National Service Framework for Mental Health in England*.

3. Department of Health (2005) *The First Five Years: Report of the National Director for Mental Health*.

4. SEU/NIMHE (2004) *Report on Social Exclusion: Department of Health/Office of the Deputy Prime Minister*.

Strategy Unit on Life Chances for Disabled People,[5] the follow-up to the Adult Social Care Green paper, stresses choice, user control, empowerment and equality. It is up to all of us who care about people with mental health problems – policy makers, providers, commissioners, communities, families and service users themselves – to work in partnership and grasp these opportunities to support our friends and loved ones to achieve their recovery goals. Georgina Wakefield's account of her own family's experience gives us inspiration and practical hints on 'how to'. It is an invaluable resource. Sometimes we ask ourselves the rhetorical questions 'If I had my time again?' or 'If only I knew then what I know now'. Well, as someone who has had the enormous privilege of being involved in mental health care development in the last few years, if I had 'my time again' – knowing 'what I know now' I'm pretty clear about what I would have done:

I would have placed greater prominence on recovery as a central tenet of mental health policy. I would have put greater emphasis on equality, tackling discrimination and promoting inclusion. I am proud that I still have the chance to support such important actions, which in turn will improve the experience of people with mental health problems. Above all people's experience (because that is where expertise truly comes) needs to be brought centre stage of policy and service development. User and family feedback should direct us, not offend us. As you go on to read the poetry, stories and observations in this book you will be enlightened and encouraged to do more ... I was.

---

5. www.cabinetoffice.gov.uk/media/cabinetoffice/strategy/assets/disability.pdf

# Introduction

**THE CARERS' MOTTO:**

*HE WHO SHOUTS LOUDLY GETS HEARD*

I was inspired to write this book by Christian. Our journey spans two decades. I say 'our journey' because my whole family have been affected. Christian's courage has given me the determination to try my best to get some long overdue respect for those who are unlucky enough to become part of such a tragic life event.

**A MESSAGE FROM JULIA BILECKYJ***

Schizophrenia is a chronic disabling disease and one of the most devastating of all illnesses, causing incalculable suffering to both patients and their families. This book is reflective of a journey that unfortunately far too many patients and their families have to make. The book encapsulates the hopelessness of the situation, the frustration and finally the glimmer of hope as the whole family slowly move forward on the long road to recovery.

Schizophrenia is far more common than most people realise, affecting 1 in every 100 people worldwide (more people than Alzheimer's disease or multiple sclerosis), people in all cultures and in all social classes and yet the general public knows very little about it and it's rarely publicised. Patients can and do improve enough to lead independent and satisfying lives. One of the keys to this is medication appropriate to the individual's needs. Clozaril/ clozapine is known as the gold-standard therapy for treatment-resistant schizophrenia, and yet it took seven years and a mother's unwillingness to give up before it was prescribed for her son. As

---

\* Julia Bileckyj is a qualified nurse who also works in management consultancy.

such, it is a tragic indictment of the current public health system – which works so well for some and so poorly for others.

This book is a counterbalance to the negative perceptions all too often portrayed in the media. Those of us who work closely with the NHS know that work is progressing on disseminating best practice; this story shows that it cannot afford to wait or to fail and policy makers and health service managers should read this book if they are in any doubt whatsoever.

# Glossary

| | |
|---|---|
| ADHD | Attention deficit hyperactivity disorder |
| APU | Anglia Polytechnic University |
| ASW | Approved social worker |
| BPC | British Psychoanalytic Council |
| BFT | Behavioural family therapy |
| CMHT | Community mental health team |
| CPA | Care plan approach |
| CPN | Community psychiatric nurse |
| CPTSD | Complex post traumatic stress disorder |
| CSIP | Care Service Improvement Partnership |
| DID | Dissociative identity disorder |
| DLA | Disability living allowance |
| DP | Direct Payments |
| DSS | Department of Social Security |
| EE | A term used by professionals for high expressed emotion |
| EPA | Eicosapentaenoic acid |
| HAFAL | A mental health charity in Wales |
| IoP | Institute of Psychiatry |
| MIND | Leading mental health charity for England and Wales |
| NICE | National Institute for Health and Clinical Excellence |
| NIMHE | National Institute for Mental Health in England |
| OT | Occupational therapist |
| PALS | Patient advice liaison service |
| PCT | Primary care trust |
| RETHINK | Name of the biggest mental health membership charity in England |
| TIM | Tormented insecure mind; interpreted in this way to help carers to understand the psychotic process |
| TOM | The 'other mind' |
| TRS | Treatment resistant schizophrenia |

# 1

# Proud

## HOW WE FEEL ABOUT CHRISTIAN

**PROUD**

Our youngest son Christian John
Suffers from schizophrenia
He suffers each day in silence
With a kind and gentle demeanour
But look deeply beyond his label
To the baby I held in my arms
To the happy, mischievous 4-year-old
Who captured the world with his charms
To the bright, intelligent 10-year-old
Who excelled at school in his study
To the 12-year-old football fanatic
Who'd come home exhausted and muddy
To the carefree, handsome teenager
Who'd greet me each day with a kiss
To the son I'd lay down my life for
And the man I was destined to miss
He waded through the torment
Hallucinations and angry voices
Robbed of the sweet years of youth
And denied so many choices
He dealt with public ignorance
And the pain that goes with stigma
He accepted that mental illness
Is viewed as a kind of enigma
Because our son was sent on a journey
There were demons he had to face
Along with horrific memories
He struggles each day to erase
A journey so long and relentless
We can never measure his pain

So many times he'd stumble and fall
Then rise to his feet yet again
Now he's quiet and unassuming
But to us he stands out in the crowd
He's the son he was always destined to be
And one word describes our feelings
And that's PROUD

The most important thing for carers to remember is never give up HOPE. Readers will be able to see the change in the whole family as our journey takes its course. You will read about the importance of having time to discuss our needs. A positive attitude is vital but can often take a long time to achieve. During the early years due to lack of understanding, information and support my own negative attitude often made it harder for Christian to recover. I was petrified of schizophrenia which produced a mirror image of his fear; he would look to me for reassurance and support but he could see my fear staring back at him. We needed far more guidance, we needed to know what we were dealing with. Life just went on and on …

### THERE BUT FOR THE GRACE OF GOD GO I

Can there be a harder journey than that for those who lose their minds?
Can you grasp the slightest inkling of their pain?
Hallucinations, angry voices invade their precious time
Forcing fragile minds to go insane
Is there a less demeaning label than Paranoid Schizophrenic?
Would you spare the time to listen to their stories?
Schizos, psychos, nutters described so often by the media
To make them sound more dangerous, more gory
Can there be anything that strips us of our precious self-esteem
Than the ignorance that surrounds mental distress
Surviving every day by the sheer skin of their teeth
Yet they're made to feel that they are even less
Less than human beings, they're weirdos, screwballs, loonies
They're a waste of space, they're crazy, they're insane
Can there be a harder journey than that for those who lose their minds?
Can you grasp the slightest inkling of their pain?
They lack all motivation but somehow they survive
They accept that people just can't understand
Get well cards and flowers are thin upon the ground
And the support and comfort of a caring hand
Can there be a bleaker outlook than for those who lose their minds?

We should marvel at their strength to face each day
They're the bravest human beings, they deserve so much respect
Fate has dealt them all such painful cards to play
The side effects of medication are the lesser of two evils
Sheer resilience is mixed with fear and dread
They don't have any choices and they're very much aware
At least it dulls the voices in my head
Can there be a harder journey than that for those who lose their minds?
We should listen to their desperate silent screams
We should put ourselves in their shoes if only for one day
Reflect on all those shattered hopes and dreams
Can there be a harder journey than that for those who lose their minds?
Compassion, kindness far too long overdue, one in four develop mental illness
No one is immune, remember one day this could easily be you
They didn't choose this journey or this tragic life event
Lives changed forever in the blinking of an eye
So support them and respect them and remember these few words
There but for the grace of God go I

## WALKING THE WALK: EMPATHY

### THERE'S NO SUBSTITUTE FOR EMPATHY
There's no substitute for empathy please try to share my views
If only you could slip them on and walk a mile in a carer's shoes
There's no substitute for knowing that someone else has walked your road
Like you they've cried a million tears on their backs a heavy load
I'm aware how hard you've tried to learn what it takes to be a nurse
But I can't convey the onslaught that's part and parcel of this curse
I cannot help you understand what it's like to share this plight
Can you see the painful shackles within another carer's sight
I know you do your level best to assist us on our route
But when it comes to sharing empathy, there is no substitute

Carers are cost effective. A good NHS Trust knows that it's wise to take care of carers:

### A MEAGRE COST
If you're wise you'll take care of your carers
Because carers really care
Miraculously 24/7 carers are always there
Carers prevent a relapse time and time again

Carers provide such solid support
They cope with the pain and the strain
But carers need to stay healthy
We just can't afford to be ill
Even though our lives are affected
Carers keep caring still
Carers are cost effective
Reassuring by night and by day
Costing £53 10 pence a week
Such a paltry price to pay
Compare that to the price of inpatient care
Or a fully qualified CPN
Years of training – diplomas – degrees
Now do your sums once again
If you're wise you'll take care of your carers
Carers provide the key
We can provide something vital
And essential to recovery
If you're wondering what that something is
Be assured it cannot be bought
And no matter how many books you read
That something cannot be taught
Because love is the magic ingredient
Without it we'd all be lost
So if you're wise you'll take care of your carers
Then simply measure the meagre cost

- By doing the job they do, carers save this country an estimated 87.4 billion pounds each year.

- Carers Allowance is £53 10p per week, less than Job Seekers Allowance.

- We are only entitled to one allowance despite the fact that many carers care for more than one person.

- Carers Allowance stops when we reach pensionable age; why when we carry on caring?

- You may be in a position where you can advise, listen to, or offer support to a carer.

- Involving carers will make your job easier and more fulfilling, as partners in care they really understand the service user's progress or deterioration.

- Carers bring subjectivity into the equation.

- Carers are able to identify issues that could have been overlooked, seeing the whole picture in both primary and secondary care.

- Carers are experts by experience – we know the warning signs.

A nurse asked me recently, 'How much do you get paid for caring for your son?' I replied, 'I have never claimed Carers Allowance because I work part-time.' He said, 'But if you were fostering a child, you would earn about £300 a week!' The word 'exploitation' springs to mind. Politicians know that carers won't go on strike.

Christian wrote these few lines during a particularly hard time; he was 19 years old at the time ...

*'Our greatest glory is not in never falling, but in rising every time we fall.'*

The stigma attached to mental illness is still very prevalent in society and yet this is the year 2010 – the age of technology!'TIME TO CHANGE' is the name of a recent anti-stigma campaign launched by 'Rethink', the largest mental health membership charity in the country. I'm a Media Volunteer for Rethink. Recently, Paul (my husband and Christian's father) and I took part in a film that helped to secure £18 million (from the National Lottery Fund) and is enabling them to conduct a four-year anti-stigma campaign. Our reasons for taking part in the DVD will become clear as our story unfolds. Christian agreed for Rethink to use a very painful incident, something that happened to him at a local swimming pool which was due to public ignorance. They employed an actor to play the part of Christian. I will never forget how I felt on this dreadful day – disgusted, saddened, frustrated and extremely angry to think that there is still so much more work to be done to change people's attitudes.

Writing has helped me to deal with my own feelings. I'm hoping this book will provide a deeper understanding of the suffering that the whole family are forced to go through.

I have dedicated a chapter to stigma and the desperate need for education. We are slowly moving forwards, but it only takes

one newspaper to use the headlines *'SWORD NUT RUNS AMOK'*
for the general public to lose confidence yet again, and then we
are all back to square one. But, what do we do about educating
people? The answer to that is, nowhere near enough! I believe that
until we tackle stigma and discrimination effectively we're on a
hiding to nowhere. Let's just try to …

### IMAGINE A NEW UNDERSTANDING

Imagine a new understanding
We've waited patiently now for years
The pain we've suffered through stigma
Creating a river of tears
Imagine holding our heads up high
No more whisperings, secrets or lies
Let's bare the soul of mental distress
No more need for its meagre disguise
Imagine that carers talk openly
We don't hide behind assumed names
We talk about loved ones with pride and respect
Long gone are the feelings of shame
Imagine a new understanding
Humility, care and compassion
Get well cards, flowers, comforting words
Will never again be on ration
Imagine that reporters change the way that they write
Words like Schizo and Psycho are finally kept out of sight
Imagine a new understanding
No more alienation from the norm
Imagine that new generations
Are educated from the day they are born
Imagine our neighbours welcoming us
No more protests as to where we reside
Social inclusion won't be an illusion
Imagine the lift to our pride
Imagine talking openly
Without fear, rejection or stigma
Imagine that people no longer view
Mental illness as an enigma
It's time for change, it's time for the truth
To relieve decades of painful frustration
Imagine we can make this reality
Not just a figment of imagination

We need to talk about mental illness far more openly. Informal and formal carers should work together as partners in care, respecting each other for our individual but equally important expertise.

Some carers feel frustrated, left out and ill informed. A conspiracy of silence amongst professionals only makes our job harder. The more carers can learn, the more information we can gather and more importantly the more we can understand this condition, the better. Ideally carers should be seen as part of the clinical team. Professionals should get to know the carers in order to improve the care provided because we're all too often misunderstood. I am aware that time and lack of resources will always be a problem. Unfortunately, some professionals see us as interfering and overbearing, but we have an in-built knowledge that should be tapped into and used. Through my own experiences and those of my sons, I have come to recognise the needs of both which has helped me to write this book. In addition, I am also able to recognise the qualities which are imperative in becoming a good mental health professional and I'm not talking about academic qualifications. I have sometimes found a support worker (who has no qualifications at all) far more helpful than a fully qualified mental health nurse or social worker.

Chapter 12, 'A Balanced Approach', was written by Dr Dianne Lefevre. We feel confident that we have produced a book which will bring at least some relief to carers who are living day to day in a state of blame, disbelief, and anxiety. Providing some answers will go a long way to helping them in the caring role, which is something none of us are remotely prepared for.

I've written four published books. The first, 'Schizophrenia – A Mother's Story', charts what life was like during the early years.

I wrote my second book, 'Addicts' Language', because Christian smoked cannabis and I was concerned about the youngsters out there who are blindly playing 'sanity roulette' and the growing body of evidence that it can (in some cases) trigger illnesses such as schizophrenia (to those who are already predisposed). When you have finished reading this book you will understand my concerns. If young people had any idea what it's like to suffer from psychosis, they would think long and hard before lighting a joint.

Having said that, we firmly believe that being a very sensitive and nervous young man, Christian started to smoke cannabis to 'fit in' with his peers and it was actually when he stopped smoking it that his illness erupted and the pot finally boiled over.

My third book, 'Schizophrenia Through The Maze', is a book

for carers. Recently, my publisher went into liquidation and I had to look for another who would be willing to take the books on and republish them. PCCS Books agreed. This is a combination of the two books which cover our journey to date. I have taken this opportunity to take some of the work out of them and replace it with information which I feel is more important and, of course, our journey of recovery has moved on.

# 2

# An Emotional Roller-Coaster Ride

Mental illness (in particular schizophrenia) is mostly talked about in hushed tones as if it's something to be ashamed of and hidden away. I feel ashamed to admit that during the early years if someone asked me, 'What's wrong with your son?' I would cautiously whisper, 'He suffers with his nerves.' These days, I tend to carry out my own survey by opening up a conversation in order to educate people about this very misunderstood condition. It's a chicken and egg situation – carers are scared to say, 'My son/daughter has schizophrenia', due to public attitudes. We should be providing education in schools so that future generations will at long last grow up with the right attitudes.

For the past ten years, using work from my books and eight films we have been involved in, including a BBC2 50-minute documentary entitled, 'My Family: Loving Christian', I have been providing training (or should I say explaining?) about the carer's perspective to mental health professionals at all levels. My aim is to deepen their understanding and improve relationships between formal and informal carers.

During our travels I have met other carers who have, like me, been on both sides of the fence having suffered mental distress themselves and then gone on to become carers. We do tend to sing from a slightly different song sheet!

I run a very small management consultancy from home entitled, 'Spotlight On Schizophrenia'. Clients include The Institute of Psychiatry where I'm involved in three courses – Enhanced Skills, Dual Diagnosis and Medication Management. This is followed up with the examination process, marking students on their interpersonal skills. I work for my local South Essex Partnership University Foundation Trust, two other NHS Trusts and a couple of universities. I also talk at many mental health conferences to try to get the carer's voice heard. Recently Chris has attended sessions himself to talk to students, which provides them with a whole-family perspective.

My family, like most, has had its share of problems and heartache. I've suffered from severe anxiety and depression for the best part of my adult life. I am still on medication today and I think I always will be. I was never actually given a diagnosis, but my moods fluctuated constantly and I can only assume that I suffer from anxiety-based manic depression.

## SCHIZOPHRENIA – THE SITUATION

- Is it a personality disorder, a mental disorder or an adjustment disorder?
- Are people more likely to harm themselves or someone else?
- What is the likelihood of developing the disease – 1 in 100, 200, or 500 people?
- Which is the most common, schizophrenia, MS or Alzheimer's disease?

## THE FACTS

- The causes of schizophrenia are not clearly understood. They are probably multiple and would include environmental, genetic, traumatic and possibly viral factors. Several books with useful information are available, see a few of them below.
- Very few sufferers harm other people. They would be far more likely to harm themselves. Tragically, 15% commit suicide, which highlights the immense pain that they are in.
- A tiny minority of homicides are committed by people with schizophrenia.
- Statistically, you are in more danger from your next-door neighbour.
- One person in every hundred people is given a diagnosis of schizophrenia – more people than people with MS or Alzheimer's disease.

I am 62 years old, married to Paul (for 44 years) and mother to two

Bentall, R (2004) *Madness Explained: Psychosis and human nature*. Harmondsworth: Penguin.
Boyle, M (2002) Schizophrenia: A scientific delusion? London: Routledge.
Read, J, Bentall, R & Mosher, L (2004) *Models of Madness: Psychological, social and biological approaches to schizophrenia.* London: Routledge.

sons: Stephen is 39 and Christian is 36. Stephen is happily married to Angela. Christian is single, works part-time and lives in his own flat (a ten-minute walk away from us). We have a Border Terrier, Alfie and an African Grey Parrot, Pepsi, who can speak in 9 different voices. When we took part in the BBC documentary I had a bet with the producer/director that I could teach Pepsi to say 'Stop the Stigma' within a few days and he was filmed a few days later doing just that!

I believe that my formative years have had a big impact on my role as both a mother and carer, which is why I have written a little about them to try to explain. I have been part of a carers' group for the past three years. The group is facilitated by a group analyst and the sessions run for one-and-a-half hours on a weekly basis. It was during these sessions that I came to realise just how much my childhood has impacted on my adult life.

## AN ANALOGY

Recently I was walking my dog along the beach at Grays in Essex where we live. Don't imagine a beautiful sandy beach, it's quite the reverse! I noticed the debris and the driftwood amongst the murky waters and how, when the tide was going out, bits of rubbish, wire shopping trolleys, jagged pieces of glass, etc, were left sticking up out of the sand. As the tide rolled in again, it covered them up and it looked calm and tranquil again. I likened the scene to mental distress, the painful uncomfortable feelings would come and go but the ugly jagged pieces are still there underneath, waiting to resurface again and again, causing emotional distress.

THE DEBRIS AND THE DRIFTWOOD

The debris and the driftwood, jagged, sharp, and ugly
Stick out painfully amongst the sand
Like a man who's slowly drowning
But no one's there to hear his screams
Or see the waving of his frantic hand
As the tide rolls in, it covers up the debris
But it lurks silent furtively still under there
It disrupts our raw emotions, stirs them up and causes pain
Then it rushes out again without a care
We're left to feel abandoned, fear and dread set in
We're washed up on this littered ugly shore

Like the scene that's in our mind's eye
The debris and the driftwood
We often feel that we can take no more
To recover from our pain
We have to sort through all the debris
Make it safe for us to walk along the beach
To see the beauty in the driftwood
In its shapes and in its colours
The 'joys' in life no longer out of reach

Each painful experience becomes part of our being, each piece of driftwood a memory that stays within us, moulding us into the adults we finally become, similar to post-traumatic stress disorder. These feelings become entrenched, like the debris even though it's constantly kicked around it stays put, deep within us. As the waves go back out, the feelings subside, only to come back in again and again during the course of a lifetime.

When it becomes too painful to bear, we're often given medication. To be honest, there were times that I was extremely grateful to be able to take a pill to dampen the feelings down. But isn't it a bit like treating the plant above root level? The cause of the pain starts at the root; medication purely masks the problems. Talking therapies have helped both me and Christian, but sadly for many people, it's a luxury that the NHS can ill afford. Having someone to talk to and unload our feelings to is imperative to mental well-being. Recently a professor of psychiatry asked me what I thought had helped my son on his journey. I listed many things, love being the main mover, also talking therapy, part-time work, supported housing, omega-3 fatty acids – I have made a whole list at the end of this book. He replied, 'Oh dear and there was me thinking it was all down to medication.' Amazing, I thought.

Asking people to go through the pain of mental distress without the guidance of a talking therapy is like asking a mountaineer to climb the Himalayas without a map, a compass, a rope and a light – they will stumble and fall. If we're emotionally robust, we can deal with a disruptive childhood; if we're not some of us pay very dearly.

My anxiety and depression hasn't affected Stephen, but Christian is far more sensitive. I believe he picked up on my feelings and we became almost fused together over the years. I do not blame myself. I have learned through therapy that the answer is in understanding, blame is pointless. Unlike medication, it takes lots of time and patience. Unlike medication there is no quick fix.

At the age of 59 I discovered that mental distress is very prevalent on my father's side of the family. I have cousins who suffer from both manic depression and schizophrenia, so there's a definite genetic link. My mother died on January 14th 2006 and, whilst she was in hospital following a stroke, I received an email from Tony (a cousin, on my father's side) in America. Tony (who I have never met) said that he was putting together the Shinwell Family Tree and where did I fit into the tree?. We started to write to each other, exchanging news about our lives. I also received an email from another cousin, who said '*I was interested to see that you suffer from manic depression, so do I and so does my daughter. You also have a cousin whose son suffers from schizophrenia.*' For a while I just stared at the screen in disbelief. For years, my mother had wondered where this mental distress had come from. No one on her side of the family had suffered from a mental illness. My parents parted when I was seven years old. I didn't give a thought to my father's side of the family, but there it was on the screen – this was where it came from. Was my father suffering from manic depression? After years of despising him for his erratic behaviour, I now believe that he was.

Dread, futility, hopelessness, despair – these words describe what it feels like to be in the grip of emotional distress. These were the same painful feelings that I had experienced as a child. During my entire life they have purely resurfaced time and again. At the onset of my illness, when these feelings began to take hold, I was 18 years old. I have only recently come to terms with the fact that Christian is a different son. He is however, a sweet and extremely compassionate human being. If he didn't have to cope with the dreadful symptoms of schizophrenia, I can say in all honesty that I wouldn't want him to be any different.

Writing has played a big part in my recovery. I wrote about my childhood memories many years ago. I'd remember bad days and then write poems about my own feelings as a child. I even decided on a book title, 'Memories of Childhood'. Writing has helped me to make sense of things and also come to terms with the past.

When Chris became ill, it hit me like a ton of bricks. The first seven years were horrendous. I call this period the 'wilderness years'. When I look back, I still shudder at the thought of what life was like for all of us then.

If I had to take this journey again, I would be far more positive. I think my own fears and anxiety hindered Christian's recovery. This is why I would like to see an early intervention service for carers right from the start. We need a specially trained person on the wards, (preferably an experienced carer) or at least someone who has been trained by a carer. This would help new carers to cope with the trauma. Just knowing that someone understands would bring a great deal of comfort. They could point the carers in the right direction for advice and information but, more importantly, help them with hope. This post should be properly funded and I feel sure that the results would be extremely favourable.

Recovery is something that for years I never dreamt was possible. I'm not saying that life is plain sailing or that Chris doesn't experience any symptoms at all, but these days he knows how to deal with them. He's aware of what's real and also what is part of his condition.

Any mental health carer will tell you that when someone you love becomes mentally ill, you go through many stages before you finally reach acceptance. It's only recently that I have been able to accept what has happened. Due to the sadness I felt witnessing my son's life passing him by, I became overprotective. I was later to learn that being overprotective is not the answer. Let's just say that if I had to go through this again, I would handle things very differently. I also blame a lack of training, support and hope. Thank God things are improving, but there's a long way to go yet.

During the early years, I used to listen to a song by Michael Boulton entitled, 'When I'm Back on My Feet Again', and I really believed that Chris would be back to his old self in no time. This belief went on for many years.

I have met many professionals during my own illness and Christian's. The one that stands out above all the rest is Dr Dianne Lefevre. Dianne assessed Chris for Talking Therapy, which has helped us all to understand things clearly. She suggested that Chris and I attend family therapy sessions and she also set up the carers' group. All of these have helped the whole family to cope and lessen the tension or so-called 'high expressed emotion' which continually went on between us. Having someone take the time to talk over the past, talking through emotions and feelings has helped me to work through things and take stock of my own behaviour.

# 3

# Where It All Began?

To make things clear, we will go back to where I believe my mental distress began. The seeds were set when I was a child. I can vividly remember feeling depressed. I was envious of my school friends because they were smarter than me. I was very unhappy. I wasn't abused or subjected to physical violence and, compared to others I would say that life was OK, but my parents were always rowing. This was solely due to my father's behaviour. We never had holidays and he was hardly ever at home. He worked as a long-distance lorry driver and working away fitted in well with his love of women, partying and spending money as if it were going out of fashion. My mother was totally unaware that he was suffering from a mental illness.

### SCRUFFBAG

My mother met my father during the Second World War. He pursued her, even though she rejected his advances as at first she didn't like him at all. He was about 5'10", dark, handsome and full of charm. He was also extremely problematic and he continually told her lies. Mum went to see the Army Psychiatrist because my father had been discharged from the Army for going absent without leave yet again and she was worried sick about the future. He told her that, after having several sessions with my father, he believed he was a psychopath. She asked what this meant and he said, 'Your husband was born without a conscience, he can hurt people and feel no remorse at all.' She asked him if there was any treatment for it and he said, 'No, it's a personality disorder.' I believe he had bipolar disorder – perhaps he had both, who knows? My father, Emmanuelle Roche Shinwell, came from a big family. My grandfather's brother was Lord Manny Shinwell and my father was named after him. My grandparents ran a hotel in Whitley Bay, Northumberland and my mother went to stay there before they got married. She told me that his mother had a wonderful voice and would sing in the evenings to entertain the guests. My grandmother warned her many times about her son. She'd say, 'He's a bastard and I would sooner see you dead at my feet than married to him.' When he was young, my father trained to be a Roman Catholic priest but he soon dropped out of it. He could speak fluent Latin and, like me, he also loved writing.

Soon after my sister was born, my mother fell pregnant with me. I was born one year and two weeks later on October 29th 1947. Mum was very ill after the birth and spent many months in bed with pneumonia and thrombosis. She always said that this was the only period during their marriage that my father ever looked after us and that was only because he didn't have much choice. Life did not improve. Not only was my father bad with money, he had many affairs. My mother often told me that somewhere I have eight half brothers and sisters scattered around the country. He had an affair with a Major's wife (not long after they married). For years they'd been trying for a child but hadn't succeeded and my father managed to get her pregnant and split their marriage up in the bargain. According to my mother, he showed no remorse whatsoever.

From a very early age I can remember the rows. One morning mum was cooking bacon and eggs and they started to argue. As usual he was working away and was about to leave. We had three big dogs and mum hurled the frying pan at him and the contents landed on his shoulder. The three dogs were jumping up to try to reach the rashers of bacon. My sister and I would often make a camp in our bed and pull the bedclothes over our heads to shut out their raised voices. Early one summer's evening, things got out of hand and we came downstairs to see my father with his hands around her neck. She was wearing a string of tiny pearls and I can still remember the sound as they hit the tiled floor. My sister dialled 999 and the police came. We were both very scared and, as always, we comforted each other.

Like Christian, I was a very sensitive child. One of our neighbours had a finger missing and when he came round for a cuppa he would have to keep his gloves on. One day he must have forgotten and I was physically sick – my mother was most embarrassed. I developed a strange habit! It involved trying to put my finger behind my eyes. It terrified me and yet I would sort of dare myself to do it. Even in class sometimes, the teacher would shout at me, 'Georgina Shinwell will you please stop fiddling with your eyes!' I sort of wanted to get them out, but I was terrified of it actually happening at the same time. Maybe I centred all of my anxiety on it to prevent myself from thinking about the real problems at home or perhaps I was mentally trying to gouge my eyes out because I didn't want to see what was going on.

I wanted my parents to love each other, I wanted holidays like other kids, I longed to wear smart patent shoes and lily-white socks, and more than anything I felt I didn't fit in. My father was completely unreliable and would go off for weeks at a time. Mum threw him out a few times and went back on state benefits so that she could at least manage to pay the bills. Money was really tight and she wasn't able to keep buying us new clothes. My grandmother did her best and she would make dresses for us on a Singer sewing machine. One day a neighbour gave mum some clothes for us and in the bag was a pair of boys' shoes. I wanted to wear them because they were smarter than my old brown sandals. Mum tried hard to stop me from wearing them but I insisted. She said, 'The kids will laugh at you.' They were black lace-ups with punch holes in the shape of a love heart. The attraction for me was that they were so smart and shiny. The girl who sat next to me wore black patent shoes with a strap across the front. I envied her so much in her crisp white school blouse. I'll never forget the one and only day that I wore the dreaded shoes. We used to play a game called 'Pharaoh' and I asked if I could play. They started to laugh at me and one girl said, 'Look she's wearing boys' shoes.' I tried to convince them that they were girls' shoes, but they decided to be even more spiteful and joined a circle around me. They were saying, 'You're scruffy and you haven't got a dad. You're a scruffbag! Scruffbag!' After that experience, I reluctantly went back to wearing my brown sandals. Even after 50 odd years I can still see them scuffed at the toes and out of shape. It was an extremely hot day (even now I detest really hot weather) and during the break I ran to my sister for comfort. She put her arms around me and said, 'One day we'll show them that we're as good as they are.' Those words have stayed with me throughout my life. I can't bear people who belittle others, or think that they are better than anyone else.

We were about six and seven years old and one morning during another heated argument, my sister said, 'Lets go to Nan's.' Our grandparents lived about five miles away. I was scared. It was a very hot day and the huge lorries were rattling past and throwing up showers of dust. Life was so different then. If two small girls were seen in those circumstances today, people would have intervened and called the police. By the time we reached our grandparents' house, we were totally exhausted. After about half an hour there was a knock on the door and two policemen came in with our parents. My mother shouted at us at first but it was with obvious relief. Grandad didn't manage to hide his anger and told them that they should be ashamed of themselves, then we all got into the police car and went home again. I dreaded going home and wanted to stay with my grandparents; I always felt safe when they were around. Life carried on much the same – my father still kept staying away from home, still kept mum short of money and he still kept womanising. When I was five he promised to send me a watch for my birthday (he'd sent my sister a pen and pencil set two weeks before on her sixth birthday). It didn't come and from then on I always felt he loved her more than me.

They parted when I was seven; my mother had taken enough and she found the courage to tell him to go, he had lots of so-called friends who offered him places to stay and away he went.

He didn't ever pay any maintenance nor did he try to get to see us. I only ever saw him once more when I was about 16. He died some years ago and his brother told my mother that he had never changed his ways – at the age of 65 he'd been having an affair with his nephew's 34-year-old wife. When his nephew found out, he went to a local golf course, put a gun into his mouth and pulled the trigger. He once told my mother that he saw all four of us as a rosy red apple which looked really good on the outside, but inside was a huge maggot and the rotten part was him.

The Carer Therapy sessions arranged by Dr Lefevre were very revealing. We talked about anything and everything. Six mothers who were carers for a son or daughter who suffered from psychosis sharing the pain, the frustration. Soon we were able to see and feel the immense empathy we had for each other. I learned so much about myself and my behaviour during these sessions. Having the time to let this out and then listen to the others in the group was both revealing and extremely helpful.

## OVERWHELMING FEELINGS OF PROTECTION

When I was 18 and newly married my grandfather died from cancer and I went to see my GP because I became severely anxious and depressed. He prescribed Valium (tranquillisers) which took the edge off of my feelings. I managed my life in a fashion and frequently went back for more antidepressants or tranquillisers. When I was

20 I got a job working for the Fire Brigade as a mobilising officer. The duties included taking the 999 calls from the public and sending out the appliances. I had to learn to use the radios to be able to stay in touch with the appliances. It was an interesting job and very absorbing and it helped with the depression a lot. My psychiatrist said that it was a god-send. I did shift work and the nights consisted of 15 hours. Three years later, we decided to start a family and I worked for the first five months of the pregnancy. After Stephen's birth, the symptoms got worse, but I had a new baby to look after and I knew that somehow I had to cope. Luckily he was a very placid child.

Life carried on and I continued to suffer from severe anxiety and bouts of depression.


### SMILER


When Christian was born three years later, I was even more depressed following the birth. He was a beautiful baby with thick black hair. My mum said. 'He looks just like you did, except he's a boy!' At the time I had no idea why, but I had these overwhelming feelings of protection. He was such a good baby and slept right through the night from the day he was born. He was happy and contented – we nicknamed him Smiler. He weighed 8lbs 4ozs. I needed quite a few stitches and promptly developed an infection, which pulled me down even more. The overprotection thing was so strange because I didn't have it at all when Stephen was born. It wasn't that I loved him more than Stephen – love had nothing to do with it. My anxiety was just getting worse. Looking back on Christian's childhood, he was always problematic – he found it difficult to concentrate, had an overactive imagination and he didn't take well to change. When he reached the age of two, he became very difficult and extremely clingy. He couldn't bear to be parted from me, nor me from him for that matter. When he started play school at the age of three, he literally screamed the place down when I left him and all the while he was there, I would worry and fret about him. I just couldn't leave him there and forget it. According to the women that worked there, he was much the same. We felt each other's anxiety.

The mood swings continued and Paul had a hard job dealing with me sometimes. I went to relaxation classes and I can remember closing my eyes as instructed and thinking this makes no difference at all. More medication which made me feel like a zombie, one tablet in particular made me feel as if I'd been hit over the head with a cricket bat. I often experienced extremely powerful feelings of depersonalisation as if I were viewing life through a huge goldfish bowl but unable to really take part. The worst feeling by far was fear. The only way to describe it is to compare the feelings like this – if you were terrified of heights and made to stand on the edge of a tower block – this measures the intensity of my fear. Sometimes I'd have really long periods of fear. I'd wake up with it and go to bed with it – the selfsame fear that I felt when my parents were at war. I didn't want to face the day and would often just stay in bed. I found it difficult to talk to people, especially people who didn't understand, which unfortunately was most people.

Friends would say, 'You'll have to pull yourself together', or 'You've got a nice home, a good husband, lovely children, what more do you want?' I found this very frustrating. I knew that it had nothing to do with any of those things. No matter what circumstances I lived in or how much money we had, it would be there and yet there was nothing to be anxious about.

I envied other people. I so wanted to enjoy life and be free from the feelings. Life went on and somehow as a family we managed to cope. I was tried on more medications – tranquillisers, antidepressants and also lithium carbonate to level out my moods. Anxiety and depression went hand in hand – first the anxiety, then the depression. The feelings gripped me like a vice.

As predicted by my psychiatrist, the symptoms improved when I passed the age of 40. Even today I'm not 100%. Writing has helped a great deal and also getting to know myself, what I can and can't cope with. I still take Prozac (an antidepressant). I was 42 and unmedicated when Christian developed schizophrenia and I can honestly say that I'd sooner suffer myself than witness his suffering. This next poem is about how I used to feel, always waiting to feel better especially after a change in my medication – waiting, waiting, waiting ...

JUST WAIT UNTIL TOMORROW
Waiting to feel better day after day after day
These new pills will help me, silently I pray
Bitter disappointment I'm feeling just the same
Why don't I feel better, is this all part of a game?
Waiting to feel better I'm aware that I must cope
Miraculously I hold onto shattered, fragile hope

Waiting to feel better, endless futile time
Praying for a miracle, reaching the end of the line
I instruct myself stay positive, tell myself stay strong
Feeling anxious, terrified and like I don't belong
Waiting to feel better, sick of wasted days
Yet I know I must stay strong because that's the only way
Waiting to feel better, depression, sadness, sorrow
The voice of hope screams in my head just 'Wait Until Tomorrow'

Although it was hard I can say in all honesty that it was easier than witnessing my son's suffering. It felt as if Christian had been stolen from us, our hopes and dreams were totally shattered by ...

### THE ONE WHO STOLE OUR SON

You stole his life, you stole his youth, you stole his liberty
You stole the dearest precious gift that God had given me
You stole our hopes; you stole his future, demolished precious dreams
His life a jigsaw fell apart, undone at all the seams
You shattered our lives in the making, took away our hope
Two burning questions – why our son? And how will the family cope?
A kaleidoscope of thoughts and feelings, angry, hostile voices
You left him in the wilderness, denied him any choices
Horrific hallucinations invaded every day
Compassion and understanding so rarely came our way
We clung together for dear life, we leaned on one another
Anxious, depleted, terrified, father, brother, mother
This new imposter looks the same but can he really be our son?
An alien invades our lives but his battle must be won
Isolation reigns supreme, a sad subservient clone
He longed to do so many things but he was lost and so alone
We fell apart; we lost our friends, alienated from the norm
Stigma, prejudice, so inhumane, we fight another storm
We watched him suffer, saw his pain, we witnessed this endless fight
We picked him up and gave him hope to see an end in sight
We grieved for lost relationships, all the girls he would have kissed
The friends, the laughs he'd been denied and all the fun he'd missed
You watched this sheer destruction which went on and on for years
You turned the cruelest blindest eye to a river made from tears
Shell-shocked, grieving, we carried on from day to day to day
We fought this monster till at last we finally found our way
But who believed they had the right to push us all this far?
The one who stole our precious son – SCHIZOPHRENIA!

# 4

# A Mother's Story

And so the start of our journey begins with work from 'Schizophrenia – A Mother's Story', which follows Christian's journey right up till he finally became well enough to come back to live in his home town. What we weren't prepared for was both the lack of care in the community and the stigma that we were about to come face to face with. 'Schizophrenia Through The Maze' begins with Christian coming back to live in the community, but this time he would be living independently.

'One Day Mum' is the first poem I wrote about schizophrenia.

**ONE DAY MUM**
Nine long years have been and gone
Are we any further on?
The years just seem to come and go
Recovery savagely grindingly slow
People outside looking in
Can't perceive the pain I'm in
They think she's fine
They think she'll cope
I sleep, I breathe, I live in hope
I feel so sad for things you've missed
For all the girls you would have kissed
The friends the fun you've been denied
The times I've thought of this and cried
The normal things that bring us pleasure
Far too numerous to measure
Trips abroad, parties, driving
You're still in rehab always striving
Striving to be well one day
One day mum I hear you say
When I feel I can't go on
I think of you my precious son

I feel your strength that rarely falters
I wait and wait until life alters
I never ever give up hope
Because that's the only way to cope

Schizophrenia is relentless, almost cunning in the way that it lulls you into a false sense of security, only to be followed time and again by bitter disappointment. If you ask any carer, 'What is your greatest wish?' They will say, 'For my son/daughter (whoever they are caring for) to have a better quality of life.' As this book unfolds, you will see that my acceptance only became possible when Christian finally managed to achieve acceptance of his own illness and a far better quality of life many years later.

Professionals can play a very important role in the recovery process, by giving the right level of support, persevering and listening to the wants and needs of the individual. But this should also be combined with working with the family and addressing their needs and concerns too. Building a good relationship with the individual *and* the family will all go towards helping with the recovery process. There's always more going on under the surface – during long periods of nothing happening – than meets the eye. It may be a time when the person is composing their self in preparation for the next step forward – confidence-building time. I used to tell Chris to imagine a row of boxes and that he had to go from one box to another and not try to miss some out. The fear of failing is always very much present. Recovery is about finding meaning to their life and also a meaning to live.

During the past 20 years I have found the best professionals have been the ones who view the recovery process as a WHOLE FAMILY EXPERIENCE. The service user has to come first but professionals should also take carers into consideration because we also have to recover from schizophrenia. For all of us, recovery is taking one step forward and two steps back ...

NO STEPS BACK

One step forward, two steps back
Recovery's getting nearer
Two steps forwards, two steps back
The fog is getting clearer
One step forwards, one step back
We're all aware we have to cope
We can't afford to lose the sight

Of neverending hope
We've all had to recover
From paranoid schizophrenia
We've all learned how to fight
The stigma in the media
They say united we all stand
But divided we will fall
Not so with mental illness
It's not like that at all
If this monster gets too close
We all give it one hard whack
Till in the end we'll all be taking
One step forward, no steps back

Christian was (still is sometimes) plagued by his thoughts, moods or feelings and this in turn affects or should I say 'infects' his loved ones. This condition affects the very core of the sufferer. Thoughts, moods, feelings – all of the things that make us who we are. The negative symptoms are just as hard to cope with – the inertia and total lack of motivation. It's almost as if a light goes out and we're left frantically searching for the switch. More than anything I was scared of how bad things could get and also how I would cope witnessing his pain day in and day out.

To develop this condition at any age is devastating, but it's harder if you are only 15. Chris had no experience of work, socialising, driving, relationships, etc.

I get frustrated about the ignorance attached to mental illness. I was asked by a colleague at work, 'How did he catch it?' As if it were an airborne virus! In retrospect, I should have touched her arm and said, 'Just like that.' I have also been asked [many times] if my son is violent. People just assume that people with this illness are axe-wielding maniacs. All the sufferers I have met have been gentle souls. It is almost as if they have a layer of skin missing and are too good for this world.

'The Voice' was written by Jenny Lawrence, a counsellor who worked for Thurrock MIND (a local mental health charity drop-in centre). She supported me by simply listening. Jenny helped me through many bleak years. Tragically she lost her own son (aged 24) in a road accident and has since died from cancer.

THE VOICE

The phone rang that day and the woman's voice said
'My name is Georgie and I have a son'
That phone call was the beginning of a journey
Which has lasted for nine years to date
This mother, so worried about her child
'He's doing this and he's doing that'
The fear in her voice with every call
It couldn't be could it Jenny
Those dreadful words – mental illness?
Go here, talk, let professional people know, they will help
Was my response to this mother
Who was just another voice consumed with worry and fear
Its just a phase she was told, he'll grow out of it
It! What was it?
It plagued her child every day and night
I am a mother and my heart went out, unable to really help
Just hold the voice and cry and laugh with her
Through a few good times
But an awful amount of bad
I came to know this family
Mum, dad and brother
All so scared for this child, now a man
Would he ever find a place in this world where he could cope
And the demon he lived with go away
Eventually the day came
'Schizophrenia' the dreaded name
Georgie said it, her voice hollow with despair
'Now he'll get help' I said, 'hang on in there'
There's a light at the end for this man
I have watched this family fight for their beloved son
This mother who would fight the world for her child to have a life
I lost my son forever but I often wonder who got the better deal
'Jenny does it ever end?' said the voice
I have no answers but if it helps to be there I will
For as long as I can
For her voice is the voice of every mother
Of a child that has a mental illness

Hindsight is a wonderful thing. We saw him as a very sensitive child who would get more confident with age. When we went away on holiday, he hated it and he would often run away. Change did not sit well with Christian. He played up so much when we took him on holiday to Wales; he drove us mad and kept saying I want to go home. When we took him out sightseeing he ran away and Paul had to chase him. He was seven years old. The signs were there but we didn't see them ...

When he was 15 years old, his history teacher phoned me to say that something was wrong with Chris, but he had no idea what it was. He said his concentration had become very poor and that the interest he had always had for history was diminishing at an alarming rate. Although I was concerned about it, I convinced myself it was just a phase that would pass eventually. His behaviour changed slowly. Very gradually he became withdrawn, argumentative and very stroppy. He would sometimes stay away from home for days and nights on end and when he finally came back, he would offer no explanation as to where he had been.

Paul threw him out a couple of times. One morning he came back again after a few days staying God knows where. He stood in the middle of the lawn in torrential rain. For over an hour the rain was hitting the ground and bouncing back up and he just stood there, his long dark hair stuck to his face, he was absolutely saturated. He didn't seem to know what he was doing, where he was going or even who he was. His whole psyche seemed to fall apart. I would often cry and say, 'He is ill.' Somehow, deep down I knew, but because his dad had been a rebellious teenager he always came to the conclusion that he was his father's son. I do not blame Paul, it was such an easy mistake to make. It came on so insidiously, it was really hard to know what was going on. One morning Chris said to his dad, 'Something is going wrong Dad and it's not going away.'

When Chris left school, he started working at Ford Motor Company. Paul said, 'It's the first day of your apprenticeship tomorrow, be in at a reasonable time, no later than 11.30pm.' Paul was sitting by the window when he came home at 3.30am. Chris hated Fords and he'd often say, 'You don't see me on those buses, you don't know how I feel.' Still we kept praying that he would come to his senses. Finally, after about 12 weeks, lots of time off and many phone calls and excuses about stomach upsets, flu, etc. we gave in and he left.

After a while Paul got him a job at his firm as a trainee profile drawer. He had no friends because he had made up his mind one day that they were just not his type of people and he stopped seeing them. He was elated when Paul came home and said, 'I've got a job for you, you start on Monday.'

At first he absolutely excelled in his work at Paul's workplace. The boss could hardly believe how well he was doing. He said he'd never seen anyone learn so quickly. Then after about four weeks, the cracks started to show and he would lose the plot and if they asked him to do a drawing, invariably, he would get it completely wrong. The boss would go to see Paul and say, 'I don't know what's wrong with Chris, but something is going terribly wrong somewhere.' One day he came home from work and started to throw his clothes into a huge pile on the bedroom floor. When I asked him what he was doing he said the patterns on the clothes were preventing him from concentrating. I looked in the wardrobe and all that was left was a few dark plain shirts and jumpers – anything with a pattern was thrown in the dustbin.

He would sometimes stay up all night trying to work out why he couldn't get things right. One morning at 6am I caught him desperately trying to get a profile drawing right. I made him a mug of tea, which he promptly knocked over the drawing and then blamed me for it. Everything was my fault. Around this time, we found out that he believed his old mates were going to break into the firm and ransack the place. He also thought they might hurt me or his dad. Paranoia was well and truly setting in.

We foolishly took him to Devon with my sister, brother-in-law and my mum. He got worse by the day. He was reading geometry books upside down, so preoccupied that he walked out in front of cars. He went and had his hair cut in the same style as a work colleague. He even bought a pair of John Lennon glasses simply because his mate wore them. I think he thought that if he looked like his workmate he might even be able to act/work like him. He seemed to be losing all sense of himself. It was as if he was trying to create a new identity by copying other people because his own identity had disintegrated. Whilst on holiday, we tried to get him to agree to see a psychiatrist when we got home; he told us we were all mad and there was absolutely nothing wrong with him at all. Physically he was wasting away and weighed around 8 stones 3 pounds, he was trying so hard to stay sane ...

# 5

# Unless He's a Danger

This chapter is about the struggle I had to get his GP to refer Chris to a psychiatrist. By the time we got an appointment, he'd totally lost sight of reality, so much so that if we dared suggest getting him some help he would say, 'What for? It's you who needs a doctor not me; you're completely mad Mum, I'm not!'

On the first visit the GP said 'You will have to get him round here.' How I was expected to is a mystery to me because he was far too ill to be able to see that he was ill. I said, 'But my son thinks that it's me who needs to see a doctor not him.' His thoughts were so muddled that he would walk out in front of cars – a couple of times Paul had to pull him back onto the pavement. At the end of the day, how dangerous do things have to be before you are given help?

Referring him to a psychiatrist would have been plain sailing to what we were coping with at home. Chris decided that he'd like to learn some basic office skills – this was after losing his apprenticeship and before he went on medication. Whilst he was struggling to do the course we received a phone call from his tutor to say that she could see that he had problems and that he seemed unable to concentrate on even the simplest of tasks. She said that they were in touch with an excellent counsellor named Jim Cook, who had previously been a professional football coach and had coached Paul Gascoigne. He told me that Gazza was an extremely sensitive young man and that in his opinion he was heading for emotional problems later in life as he didn't think that Gazza would cope with fame very well at all. How very right he was. He tried very hard to help Chris but of course we were all unaware that this was actually the onset of a very serious mental illness. Consequently things got worse.

When I paid a second visit to my GP voicing my concerns, he was horrified that Chris was having counselling. He said that we'd probably made the situation worse by allowing the counselling sessions, but of course we were so naive back then that we didn't know where to go for help and he wasn't even listening to us. He said that before he could intervene he would have to be a danger to himself or someone else. His reluctance to refer him to a psychiatrist caused havoc. Had he listened, Chris would have been given the help he so desperately needed far earlier.

Whilst attending the classes he met a lad who had learning difficulties. He was very keen on motorbikes and Chris decided he would like to buy a trials bike. They went to the other side of London by train and his friend drove back with Chris on the back. Every time he went out on it, (despite no tuition our frantic pleas not to and wearing no protective clothing apart from a crash helmet), we'd wait for a phone call to say he'd been involved in an accident. He insisted that it helped him to think straight and it blew his thoughts away. He was trying anything that would give him some temporary relief from his racing thoughts. Inevitably at 9pm one Friday night, we got a phone call from Basildon Hospital to say that he'd had an accident. He'd been travelling down the A128 towards Brentwood when a car pulled out of Plough Lane. Chris went over the top of the car and ended up minus his crash helmet, on the other side of the road with a gash in his ankle requiring 16 stitches. The police said that it was a miracle that nothing was coming the other way. The car driver admitted liability and was charged with dangerous driving. When we arrived at the hospital he showed absolutely no emotion at all and didn't know what all the fuss was about. We knew by now just how unwell he was. We were just grateful that he wasn't badly injured or killed. He vowed that he would never ride the bike again. We did feel that we'd got off lightly due to the seriousness of the ever-worsening situation we were all in. A week before this, Paul and I were at a wedding reception, as usual we rang Stephen at about 9.30pm to see if Chris was OK. Steve said, 'No mum, he's stranded at a petrol station in South Benfleet. He's just filled his bike up with diesel and I'm on my way to pick him and the bike up.' I can remember Paul saying, 'For God's sake, what next?' Four weeks later, we went to visit my mum and Chris finally broke down. Suddenly his face crumbled and he sobbed uncontrollably. Thank God he finally admitted defeat and agreed to see a doctor. The accident had escalated his condition. I can remember that the bandage they'd put on his leg was filthy and hanging off but he hadn't even noticed.

This is what it was like leading up to finally accessing services and the conflict that went on within the family ...

### DESPERATION

Slowly but surely you're losing your mind
Watching it happen so very unkind
Your concentration is almost nil
But it's hard to convince the others you're ill
You worry too much take it from me
He's a difficult teenager like I used to be
But he's been all night pacing the floor
Please listen to me once again I implore
There's really no need you worry too much
Why can't you see it? he's right out of touch
You're over-reacting you must get some rest
Speak to the doctor that would be best
 I make an appointment for the following day
With hope replenished I silently pray


### FIRST VISIT TO GP

I'm worried about my teenaged son
Something's going very wrong
He sleeps all day he's up all night
Doctor tell me is this right?
He's probably suffering from his age
Going through that funny stage
Give him space keep out the way
He'll grow out of it one day
But he's verbally aggressive, shouts and screams
He often has horrific dreams
Sounds familiar please don't fret
There's no need for hysterics yet
I'm home again I cry and cuss
Am I making too much fuss?
Another visit try again
Doctor he's in so much pain
Doctor please listen my son's ill
Over-reacting am I still?
Surely he needs to see a psychiatrist?
That's up to him I can't insist
Thank God he's sent two social workers
Now at last we'll get some answers
Mrs Wakefield your son's quite poorly
He's very ill you saw this surely
He'll see our consultant a Doctor Lowe

He'll show us just which way to go
A course of injections in his bum
And at last we'll see our long lost son
Nine years on and we're still waiting
Nine years of anticipating

## A ZOMBIE WITH LEAD BOOTS ON

And so the day finally arrived and we took him to see the psychiatrist, we thought he'd be back to his old self in no time at all ... The psychiatrist told us that he was putting Christian on a course of injections that would help him. When I asked, 'But what's wrong with him Doctor?' He replied, 'Your son has a thought pattern disorder.' He was 16½ years old.

We feel that someone should have talked to us in far more depth so that we were at least prepared for the immense change in him. The power of these antipsychotic drugs is incredible. Overnight he went from being totally deranged, talking to himself, unable to follow a conversation to a zombie with lead boots on who slept for 16–18 hours a day – this was almost as bad as when he became psychotic. For years we believed that he would just get up one day and he'd be back to his old self. How wrong we were. And so now we had to get used to another son, another complete stranger, where was ...

### THE SON WE USED TO KNOW
Where is the son we used to know?
This one's robotic, his movements so slow
In a split second he was there for all to see
Then one small injection how can this be?
In the blink of an eye this all seems so wrong
His feet are like lead as he drags them along
His eyes are so glazed and far away
Chris are you there? I feel tempted to say
Where is the son we used to know
Has anyone seen him – where did he go?
It's not all about Christian – you're also a wife
You really must try to get on with your life
It's become an obsession and that's bad for you
And what about Stephen? He needs you too
Will his condition improve?
We really don't know
You know how it is recovery is slow

We're all trying hard – doing our best
You're not looking well – you must try to rest
Find some new hobbies – try music or art
I can't find the interest I haven't the heart
But the mother's the link for the whole family
You must try to be strong or where will they be?
But these drugs are so powerful this isn't my son
I assure you it is he's under there mum
The effects will wear off but only in time
You know how it is he walks a fine line
But where is the son we used to know
Has anyone seen him where did he go?

This poem describes the negative symptoms. These symptoms are often described by carers as even worse than the positive symptoms because they can't bear the fact that life is simply passing them by. We were either incredibly sad because he was spending his life in bed or absolutely terrified by the horrors of him hearing voices or seeing things (auditory and visual hallucinations).

### SLEEP, SLEEP, ENDLESS SLEEP

Sleep, sleep, endless sleep
Sometimes too lightly, sometimes too deep
Hours and hours of every new day
In a darkened room and out of the way
Sleep, endless sleep saps your precious time
It makes no difference if the weather is fine
At a time when life should be free from care
Should I call you again? I don't think I dare
You'll only get angry and say go away
Sleep endless sleep steals another new day
You rise around 5 I make you some tea
I say what a waste you say yes I agree
You're ready for bed at 10pm
Once more you're ready to sleep yet again
Sleep, endless sleep and I pray that tomorrow
You may get up early and stop all this sorrow
I've prayed for years though God knows why
Sometimes I question if you really try
Sleep, endless sleep and I can't understand
Why you need all this sleep when you're such a young man
One day you'll wake up out of bed you will leap

Full of life no more endless sleep
This is a dream in my soul I'll keep
That the day will come when you won't need endless sleep

This one is about everyday conversations and how they affected
my feelings and still do to this day sometimes ...

### INNOCENT COMMENTS

Innocent comments heard time and again
Innocent comments that drive me insane
'How are your boys, Are they both doing well?'
The older one's fine but the youngest is in hell
No I don't really say that though it goes through my mind
It wouldn't be fair she's just being kind
It's natural for people to ask how you are
'Is the youngest one driving, has he got his own car?'
He's been in care for almost two years
I don't say that either, I'd burst into tears
Innocent comments quite normal to ask
People blind to the fact that for me it's a task
On the surface I'm fine and coping well
I cover the hurt up so no one can tell
'My John's off to Greece flies out tomorrow
Innocent comments that cause me such sorrow
'There's a crowd of them going, a right carry on
Birds, parties, discos, if I know my John'
'My Gary's done well he's just off to Uni
He's a studious lad, not quite such a loony'
I find it so painful I wish it were you
Robbed of your youth so sad yet so true
I say no he's not driving, he's a quiet lad
She says 'Christ you're lucky my John's quite mad
He works up in town an insurance broker
Got the gift of the gab, the eternal joker'
Like an open wound that's been sprinkled with salt
No hurt is intended, it's nobody's fault
Fate dealt you a hand, we all know this well
No trips abroad, just a long trip to hell
I say I must go now, I'll see you again
She's quite unaware that I'm in this pain
Innocent comments heard time and again
Innocent comments that drive me insane

**6**

# Bad Practice

Chris was about 18 and I had to take him for his depot injection*. I ended up literally dragging him out of bed and he promptly threw up outside our neighbour's house. I told him to sit in the car while I went back indoors for a mop and bucket, cleaned it up and we carried on with the journey. As he was on strong medication, he would shake a lot, he couldn't keep his legs or his head still and I found this extremely upsetting.

Chris and I sat opposite his family therapist/CPN. Behind us were two male social workers. I was completely aghast when, after the therapy session was over, the CPN suggested that Chris drop his trousers in front of two men ...

STAND IN THE CORNER

It happened at Sunnyside on your depot day
I could not believe what I heard someone say
In the room two male social workers writing things down
I'm still appalled when I think of it now
Your head was shaking not yet used to the drug
I felt I should comfort you – give you a hug
 'Drop your trousers and stand over there
It's injection time' – you just stand and stare
My mind is screaming this just can't be right
'Is there a problem Chris? You look so uptight'
18 years old – merely a lad
Your voice was faltering – you sounded so sad
'Can we go somewhere private?' I hear you say
I'll never believe it until my dying day
The nurse escorted you out of the room
I felt so relieved we'd be out of there soon

---

* A depot injection is an injection, usually subcutaneous or intramuscular, of a pharmacological agent which releases its active compound in a consistent way over a long period of time.

As the door closed I turned around
'What the hell's going on here?' some courage I'd found
'We're trying to see if a decision he'll make'
I'm so angry I physically shake
'He's been through so much why can't you see?
He deserves to be treated with dignity'
She brings you back in, a sad look on your face
'Come on son let's get out of this place'

We kept hearing (from other carers) about a drug called clozapine. One carer told me that her son was much better following nine years of sheer hell. I can remember saying to Paul that there must be a reason why they won't try it, they wouldn't let him suffer like this if there was a drug that would improve his symptoms. Finally I made an appointment to see his GP and asked him about it. I also asked him if we could have a referral to the Maudsley Hospital because I'd heard that patients there were tried on two antipsychotics for a duration of eight weeks each and if there was no improvement, they were automatically tried on clozapine within just 16 weeks. He said, 'I'm not referring your son because I have a letter here which states that it wouldn't make any difference where you took him.' We didn't argue because we didn't even realise that it was Christian's right to have a second opinion, we simply thought, well he knows best. And so life went on ...

## A TINY CHINK OF LIGHT

When Chris was 18 he reluctantly joined the MIND gardening project after yet another failed attempt to work. He tried so hard to work and would only give up when his mental symptoms became intolerable which usually happened within about 12 weeks. He was with the group on the allotments in Whitehall Lane. Sitting there brought back childhood memories as over the other side of the allotments was my grandparents' house where I lived as a child – 90 Kent Road, Grays.

Paul had been crying the day before because before he had taken Chris to MIND he'd walked round the shop and bought a notebook and pen so that he could take notes about things he might need to remember. Paul had found this very sad so consequently, I wasn't feeling very good myself. It was a cold winter's morning and I had to take my mum to her doctor. As I drove up Whitehall Lane, I could see Chris with the gardening group. The memory that stands out most of all is 'Who can I talk to?' 'Where can I go for some comfort?' and 'What in God's name can make me feel better?' (short of a miracle).

GRITTING MY TEETH FOR THE FIGHT

I feel cold as I watch from the car
You've a woolly hat over your ears
As I watch you digging the ground
I can't possibly stop the tears
The ground is very hard
Similar to your life
Acceptance is so far removed
Though reality cuts like a knife
This life isn't what we've planned
It's nothing like it at all
Things were going so well
Then we all hit a giant wall
We hit it with so much force
That it shattered us to the core
Left us in disbelief
Wondering what it's all for
But still you keep digging away
You work alongside the others
I think about their lives too
The effects on their fathers and mothers
They must find it as hard as we do
They share our relentless pain
They must try to work out why it's happened
Over and over again
They've advised us to join a group
Try to share our worries and fears
But we still can't believe it's true
So it's falling on very deaf ears
Can you see how it would help
Seeing so many others in pain?
I shudder at the thought
As I notice it's started to rain
You're cupping a mug of tea
Leaning against your spade
You're not even aware that I'm here

Oblivious to how hard I've prayed
You're wearing fingerless gloves
A present from Christmas last year
Why do they make me feel sad?
I brush away yet another tear
Then a sudden spark of hope
As I watch you all digging the ground
It ignites new inspiration
As I see the courage you've found
Behind the blackened clouds
Shines a tiny chink of light
I start up the car to go home
Gritting my teeth for the fight

During the first seven years Chris lived with us at home I made far too many mistakes. I would try to find friends for him, I'd try to find work for him all the time thinking that this was the answer and that I was doing the right thing. We were totally oblivious to what was lying ahead and to how distressed he really was. All Chris wanted to do was to stay in bed and be left alone. Summertime was the worst. I so wanted him to enjoy his life but for him that was far too hard a call. I would often go into his room and try to get him up. Paul would tell me to leave him alone, but I just couldn't bear his life passing him by. During the seven years leading up to the relapse he was tried on one other antipsychotic (olanzapine) but it didn't improve his condition at all and within a matter of weeks he was back on the depot injections again.

## BEWARE OF UNREALISTIC AMBITIONS

*If only, if only, if only*, I have said these words so many times. If only someone had sat us down and said 'Whatever you do, don't burden your son with your own unrealistic ambitions.' Because we weren't given a diagnosis for years and no one took the time to say, 'Look this is schizophrenia, it's a very serious condition. Your son needs lots of time to recover. He needs to do things at his own pace and always remember this *"if he could he would and when he can, he will"*.' He looked like the same son but of course he was very different. Carers are in such a state of bewilderment themselves, they do not relate to confusing terminology such as 'auditory and visual hallucinations'. Everything needs to be simplified because new carers are dealing with far too much emotional turmoil to even begin to take things in or even try looking for information. It felt almost like a cloak of secrecy was hanging over all of us. The training that I have seen over the years for carers is very good but for new carers I think it's all far too complicated. Yes they need to learn about side effects, meds, looking after themselves, etc., but much later on. Right at the start I would like to see training sessions that are simplified in order for new carers to slowly and with lots of support come to terms with the enormity of their situation and learn how to care at the right pace for the person they are caring for. Now 20 years on, we are of course empowered carers but it's taken many years to get to this point. Far more emotional support is needed, especially in the beginning – this is after all a bereavement. Even these days sometimes I think of Chris when he was 15 and the type of person he was then and I cry. When I think of the things I did (for years), e.g. finding him part-time work that he couldn't possibly cope with, trying to make friends for him, all because I believed that I had the answers and that what I was doing would help him. Yes I was overinvolved, yes I caused him even more anxiety but I had no idea what I was dealing with, all I could see was his whole life passing him by.

As far as giving a diagnosis is concerned, I think each family situation should be treated individually. Professionals need to GET TO KNOW the family in order to decide, 'Yes this is the window of opportunity that we have been waiting for, this is the right time for us to talk to the family about the diagnosis'.

I do take some of the blame. I should have been asking far more questions instead of burying my head in the sand, but in all honesty part of me didn't want to know that my son was suffering from schizophrenia and who would? I needed help with coming to terms with it. There were mistakes on both sides and hopefully this highlights what needs to change ...

### DIAGNOSIS, WHAT DIAGNOSIS?

Diagnosis, what diagnosis? No one's ever said
Round and round in circles, round and round my head
Diagnosis, what diagnosis? No one talked to me
I needed help to understand I'd lost the vital key
Diagnosis, what diagnosis? I didn't know the truth
And yet he suffers so much pain, he's missed out on so much youth
Diagnosis, what diagnosis? We overhear the word psychosis
But we were just his carers and no one seemed to notice.

## IT'S GOOD TO TALK

It's good to talk and recognise the importance of carers and professionals working together, interacting with each other, learning from each other and talking to each other. These are some of the questions that we should have been asking and, given the right support, we would have been asking years before we did:

### Diagnosis
- What is the diagnosis?
- How have you reached this conclusion? Signs? Symptoms?
- Can you tell me something about the causes?
- What happens now?
- What is the prognosis?
- Where do I obtain further information?
- If you haven't yet made a diagnosis what are the possibilities?
- Will you make a diagnosis in the near future?
- What advice/help can you offer me to deal with this situation?

### Assessments
- What tests will be done?
- Will further tests be needed?
- When you have the test results how will you act upon them?

### Care and treatment
- What about care and treatment?
- Who will be the care co-ordinator and what part will he/she play?
- Will anyone else be involved? How often will they see him/her?
- How long will the treatment last?
- What are the plans for the future?
- What about talking therapies, are they available? How do I go about getting them?
- What plans are in place if he/she refuses treatment?
- Who deals with the care plan? Can I see a copy of the care plan?

### Involving the family
- Can the family be involved in discussions concerning his/her treatment (assuming that they do not have any objections)?
- Is there a family group therapist that we can be referred to? And how do we access this service?

- Is there a carer support group in my area?
- Who will help if we are worried about something?
- Who do we contact in an emergency?
- We are entitled to a second opinion, but how do we go about it?

## Medications
- What medication is he/she going on?
- Why this medication and what are the short- and long-term benefits of it?
- Tell me about any side effects short and long term.
- Will he/she be on it for life?
- What if this one doesn't work? Tell me about some alternatives.
- What signs or symptoms will be indicators that the drug is not working well?
- What happens if he/she refuses to take the medication?
- Where can I get more written information on this drug?

## Hospital admissions
- What happens if there are no beds available?
- Tell me about length of admission.
- What about arrangements for coming back home?
- Will it be possible for him/her to be housed near to us?
- How do I go about sorting out his/her benefits whilst in hospital and after he/she comes home?
- When he/she is ready to come home, what will be available in the way of support and housing in our area?

# 7

# Still in the Dark

My sister found herself in a dilemma because she'd spoken to her psychiatrist about Christian and he told her that from what she'd told him (she told him the name of the meds Chris was taking), it sounded as if her nephew had schizophrenia. She felt she should tell us because we were still in the dark about the diagnosis, even though to everyone else it was blatantly obvious.

I did ask his nurse once (the same nurse who asked him to drop his trousers). I was petrified but somehow I found the courage and just blurted it out, 'Just tell me, has my son got schizophrenia?' Her reply? 'YOU TELL ME!!' Not exactly helpful and all it did was cement my denial even further – it was just something he would grow out of eventually. Part of me wanted to know the truth and yet I was terrified at the same time. I was in complete denial for years and years.

In a way it is very commendable that some psychiatrists refuse to label people, but on the other hand how do you deal with something as complex as this when you don't even have a clue what you're dealing with? Life went on, then one morning I received a letter from the DSS. It stated in black and white that Christian John Wakefield suffers from 'PARANOID SCHIZOPHRENIA'. I can remember dropping the letter and crying. I always had help from his nurse or social worker to fill in the forms. I remember thinking 'What does psychosis mean?' I openly admit that we were in denial and we'd chosen to bury our heads in the sand, but we also feel that we desperately needed support with coming to terms with this. There has to be a better way.

And so the day finally dawned. The letter prompted us to make an appointment with Christian's GP. Christian was 22 years old. His GP spoke to us very candidly, 'You do realise that your son suffers from paranoid schizophrenia don't you?' It was too much to take on board. This is how he explained Christian's inability to concentrate and follow a reasoned argument with us. Call it an idiot's guide if you like but it helped. He said to visualise a game of battleships. He drew a box with squares in it, in the squares he put capital letters and said M is for Mother, B = Brother, W = Work, S = Socialising and F = Father. This small diagram helped us to understand what Chris was going through – this is what I mean by simplifying things for carers. He went on to explain that most people are able to channel their thoughts correctly but Chris was not able to because one of his symptoms was 'thought pattern disorder'. Therefore, he explained, his brain will often flit from one subject to another, making it almost impossible to concentrate, which explains why many people can't work or study. At last we could see why he'd never been able to hold down a job for very long. Just a simple little drawing, but it revealed so much. How helpful it would have been if someone had taken the time to explain thought pattern disorder, it would have saved so much confusion. The GP said, 'Needless to say, his life and your lives will always be difficult.' It was only then that we started to take in the seriousness of the situation that we were in.

I liken this situation to reading an instruction manual to a mobile phone, a VCR or computer or alternatively someone physically showing you how to use one of them. This very simple diagram helped us both to imagine what it must be like from the sufferer's point of view. We both feel that if someone had taken the time to explain everything to us years before, it would have given us a much better understanding and the high expressed emotion would have been lessened. The many arguments that went on were due to the fact that we didn't have any understanding of what our son was going through. After we left the surgery to make our way home, Paul stopped the car. We needed time to take in the seriousness of the situation. I can still remember the many times that we've driven out to the countryside and just sat staring into space in utter disbelief, but at least we had each other. I can't even contemplate going through something like this without having the comfort that there is one other person on this earth that totally understands what it is like to be in this pain.

We sat there staring into space trying to come to terms with the enormity of our situation. At long last, thank God we were at least
...

**UNITED**
We're sitting outside the park
Both staring in disbelief
United in our plight

United in our grief
It can't be schizophrenia
This is far too hard to take
The son that we've both nurtured
There must be some mistake!!
We cling to one another
Sadness overflows
I know exactly how he's feeling
Only he and I could know
The depth of so much sorrow
The core within the pain
When hope eludes us both
Time and time again
At least it's brought us close together
Not driven us apart
This love we share for Christian
We both feel from the heart
I can feel his body shaking
Tears for his long-lost son
I tell him to keep fighting
In this war that must be won
Sometimes he's the strongest
It just depends upon the day
His turn to lift my spirits
Keep negativity at bay
What would I do without him?
The times I've wondered this
I wipe away his tears
He repays me with a kiss
Amidst the sadness I take comfort
In knowing till the end
That my husband, Christian's father
Will always be my friend

Christian's isolation continued, years of nothingness, no friends, no fun, no life. Saturday nights were even more painful, when young people were out enjoying themselves. Now and then he would try ringing old school friends. They knew he'd been ill and would fob him off saying, 'Sorry, we've already made arrangements to go out.' I'm not really sure what Chris thought.

**SATURDAY NIGHT** (Written at 1am on 26th September 1999)

It's Saturday night, yet another one
It's Saturday night and you're robbed of your fun
It's Saturday night and you're stuck in with us
You just accept it, you don't make a fuss
As you grew older we'd often say
This one will break some hearts one day
But that didn't happen, it wasn't your fate
We've tried to stay patient through such a long wait
So we just carry on in the hope that one day
With the right medication this will all go away
You'll just swallow a pill to put things right
Then it won't be another Saturday night

## A GLIMPSE OF WARD 12 – BACK ON THE SLIPPERY SLOPE

'A Glimpse of Ward 12' is about a very bad day when Steve took us to hospital so that Chris could have his depot injection increased because he was so unwell. On the way home Chris said that he could see muppets in the car and that the colours were beautiful; perhaps this was due to the higher dose of medication bringing relief from some of the symptoms. He was 20 years old and we both got …

**A GLIMPSE OF WARD 12**

We've been up all night – I can see you're unwell
Jabbering on – that's how I can tell
You run on incoherently about your sad past
Slowly getting nowhere fast
Feeling exhausted – I must think this through
I must stay strong to sort it for you
I ring the centre – He's not well at all
I'll page his nurse and ask her to call
She rings about 10 – 'How is he?' she says
I know this will be just one of those days
'Take Chris to Ward 12 and they'll sort him out'
'Get me some help mum' – 'OK Chris don't shout'
'Have you got transport?'
'Yes, my older son'
'Steve can you help us?'
'Of course I can mum'

We walk through the passageways
Strange floors – they're bright blue
Two cleaners stand chattering
We walk on straight through
The nurse says 'Sit there'
I'll be as quick as I can
We'll up your depot
To calm you young man
A sigh of relief as the needle goes in
So very much son for you to take in
The pain you have taken for so very long
You've not had a choice, you've had to stay strong
Still things could be worse, you don't have to stay
Shudder the thought you may have to one day
'Thank God you're on lates Steve, are you feeling alright?'
'Just a bit shaken at my brother's plight,
God he copes well mum people don't know
I'm amazed at his courage he's quite strong you know
I'm so proud of him mum he seems calmer now
It's a miracle he copes, I'll never know how'
I think he's grown used to it over the years
'Chris go and lie down come on dry those tears'
'Did you ring dad, mum? Shall I ring him at work?'
'No leave him for now Steve it'll only cause hurt'
'Have to go now mum – I'm on 2–10'
I say 'Thanks for your help son' and we're crying again

## A HOLIDAY AND A NIGHTMARE

I describe what you're about to read as 'the worst night of my life'. If ever a GP should have been severely reprimanded it was this one. At the time we were in no fit state to fight back. If it happened now I would not hesitate in making a formal complaint to the General Medical Council.

A dystonic reaction* (a side effect of medication) is a very frightening and painful experience physically and emotionally, both

* Dystonia is a syndrome of spasms and sustained contractions of the muscles. These muscle movements are not under voluntary control and they result in repetitive movements of parts of the body or persistently abnormal postures. www.netdoctor.co.uk/diseases/facts/dystonia.htm

for the patient and for the people witnessing it. Christian was 21 years old.

I can honestly say that before this happened we'd never even been warned that it was a possibility. I've since been told that the odds it can happen are extremely high but nevertheless we feel horrified that no one even thought to mention it. At least we'd have known what was going on and we would have had some idea what to do. The GP who finally came out to see our son was arrogant and rude and he showed absolutely no compassion whatsoever. The first time we rang, he refused to come out even though I pleaded with him. All we could do was watch Christian whose body was contorted. We were all petrified and unable to do anything at all to help him, a totally unforgettable experience. I thought he was having a fit and could possible die. When the GP finally came, he said, 'For God's sake you lot, pull yourselves together.' Paul and Stephen were both in tears and Chris was still twisted up on the floor in the kitchen. He said to get him to A&E at Basildon where they would 'zap him'. He told Christian to stand up. He struggled to his feet, but he was unable to keep his balance because his right foot was suspended and no matter how hard he tried to keep it on the floor, it just kept rising. The GP kept saying, 'Foot to the floor Christian! Foot to the floor!' This was an emergency situation and he treated us as if it was something quite trivial. When I enquired what 'zap him' meant, he said, 'They'll give him an injection which will go straight to his brain and release the dystonia.'

Thank God Stephen was there to hold onto Chris as he kept trying to open the car door and get out. I posted a letter and this poem to the GP five years after it happened in the hope that I wouldn't feel so angry and hurt. In Anne Deveson's book ,'Tell Me I'm Here', her experience of a dystonic reaction was very different from mine. She took her son to hospital and said the young doctor who saw him was very kind. He said to her son, 'This must be so very painful and distressing.' Anne said those few kind words helped so much and this is really all that's needed.

My memory of that night is as vivid as ever. I wrote the GP a letter and sent him this poem. He sent back a very curt reply thanking me and stating that I'd given him 'food for thought' – an apology would have been too much to expect, just 'I'm sorry for the distress I caused'.

**A TRIP TO DYSTONIA** (Written June 13<sup>th</sup> 1999 during the night)

We'd been to Dorset I recall
A tragedy we went at all
Thirteen people hell for you, a terrible mistake I knew
You barely ate or slept at all
Gradually climbing up the wall
Your eyes dart round from one to another
From cousin to auntie from father to mother
'Let's go home son it's best not to stay'
'No mum you need this holiday'
At last we're home and what a relief
But what happened next was beyond belief
We start to unpack, you're looking so sad
'Mum do you think I'm going mad?
I just saw a monster out there in the hall'
'No son I don't think you're mad at all'
'I could see the saliva between its teeth
I was so terrified I shook like a leaf'
'The monster's your illness showing itself
But you're clearly unwell so I'll get you some help'
I rang his GP for some more medication
Hoping it wouldn't cause too much sedation
Shouldn't do said the doctor it will just calm him down
Just leave him quiet I'm sure he'll come round
I hear you calling me from your bed
'Mum something's wrong with my neck and my head'
Your head was grotesquely turned around
Your right foot suspended away from the ground
God what's happening to our lad
I'll ring the GP – 'Steve go get your dad'
It's the same GP he sounds harassed
'Give him two Procyclidine' help at long last?
He refused yet again to come out to our son
God will this battle ever be won?
Half an hour later and things get even worse
God how I hate this evil curse
I rang him again at 11.30
At last he arrives and acts very shirty
'Come on you lot get it together'
It's so obvious we're at the end of our tether
Such sweet compassion I still can't take in
Can he not see the state we're in?

'Get him in your car you'll need A&E
They'll zap him and that will set it free'
Paul drives a bit recklessly, smokes a cigar
Christian is frantic to get out of the car
'Mum he's trying to get out of the door'
'We're almost there Steve' Can we take any more?
At last the injection, you don't make a sound
The nurse pats your bum he'll soon come around
We wait 30 minutes, the dystonia goes
Sadly and silently make our way home
We're home about 1am and straight to bed
Too shocked to speak so nothing is said
We must put this behind us and look to tomorrow
A TRIP TO DYSTONIA AND TOO MUCH SORROW!!

This poem is about the difficulty I had during the first eight years to say the word 'schizophrenia'. It also highlights how confused I was and the need for carers to be listened to and spoken to.

### THE WORD

Schizophrenia!!! There it's done
Doesn't quite roll off my tongue
Eight years it stayed within my mouth
I couldn't quite manage to spit it out
A sad achievement but there it's done
A label for my precious son
We thought naively they'd be able
Within weeks to make you stable
Sadly you sleep your young life away
Sixteen hours on average every day
Now you're timid, quiet, subdued
Not fiery, angry, hyper, rude
My senses scream, my senses shout
For God's sake what's this all about?
Wondering endlessly what this curse is
Depot injections and psychi nurses
Mrs Wakefield try not to worry
We're doing all we can, we're sorry
You know there's not a magic pill
Now calm down or you'll both be ill
Make an appointment see your GP

This is bad for Christian can't you see
GP gave me Prozac and after a while
I'm flying high I wear a smile
But we're both exhausted from the strain
We watch you struggle feel your pain
Split mind? split personality?
Get the leaflets then you'll see
Or just ask me I've read them all
It's really not like that at all
For all the sufferers I have met
One thing strikes me I can't forget
Their sweet natures shine on thru'
Thru' all their pain and anguish too
They've a God-given gift – humility
So much more than you or me
So try to learn don't turn away
Who knows this could be you one day

# 8

# A Relapse is Looming

---

December 1997 ... not such a happy Christmas! This is about a crisis situation and what it was like for all of us during a relapse. I can see now that Chris was slowly going downhill after Stephen left home in May 1997. Chris was 23 years old. In the August I found some writing he'd done on an old Mother's day card. It was a very large card and it was filled with what I can only describe as 'gobbledygook', not one line made sense. This clearly shows the state of his mind and how near he was to a relapse.

We should have known that Stephen leaving home would affect him, after all his brother was the only young person in his life and had been for seven years. Christmas was approaching and his condition was getting worse by the day. Around mid-December we made an emergency appointment to see his nurse, but there were more shocks to come.

During the week leading up to the relapse, he flooded the bathroom (twice) after leaving the plug in the sink. Another evening we took him out for a ride to Brentwood. He was last out of the door and when we got home some two hours later, the front door was wide open. Eventually Paul had no choice other than to take him to hospital. This was ...

SCHIZOPHRENIA AT CHRISTMAS TIME
Christmas, festivities, such happy times
But for you the ultimate nightmare
Festivities aggravate symptoms
Intrusive, painful, unfair
Distortion in every bright bauble
Taunting voices not jingle bells
Whilst we bathe in the pleasures of Christmas
You survive in your own private hell
We enjoy the getting together
Close family for company

Good food, a few laughs, Christmas crackers
Twinkling lights, decorations, a tree
You unwrap your brightly wrapped presents
Excitement eludes you again
You try hard to show some interest
We manage to hide our pain
You say you don't feel very hungry
You go up to lie down on the bed
Yet again schizophrenia spoils your time
But we're aware you must sort out your head
Relapse was merely a whisper away
How on earth could we be so blind?
We just couldn't cope with the reality
Yet again you were losing your mind
We struggled to assist your enjoyment
We assured you that things would be fine
But lurking within the festivities
Was schizophrenia at Christmas time

On December 27th 1997 Christian went into an acute ward. He didn't come home again for five years. He was 28 years old before he came home again ...

**RELAPSE**

I wasn't there when they took you in
I wanted to be but I couldn't have been
We'd sat up smoking night after night
Just couldn't cope so I gave up the fight
The night before at A&E
A duty psychiatrist we had to see
She sat writing notes about things you were saying
Me? I just sat there silently praying
Praying they wouldn't suggest you stay in
But I knew they could see the state you were in
I recall the doctor had a very bad cold
She was Jamaican – not very old
She talked to her colleague about going away
Said she needed the rest and was going next day
It seemed so ironic
As I knew the feeling
But I chose to stay quiet
And stare at the ceiling

Night after night I'd been without sleep
Such a strong inclination to collapse in a heap
She asked lots of questions – referred to your notes
Blew her nose constantly and cleared her throat
As she turns the pages I can see
Lots of letters to the consultant from me
I can see them clearly through my tears
Letters I've written over the years
After much pleading she lets you come home
Armed with two Ativan to help calm you down
A giant mistake and still you're not well
We've prolonged the agony I can tell
Not looking forward to the next morning
Totally exhausted – constantly yawning
Emergency appointment to see your nurse
With each second that passes things only get worse
We'll meet at the centre – be there by 10
Paul takes the day off to support us again
She's late arriving – still nothing new
You're looking quite ill and I worry for you
At last we're seated – 'What's the problem?' she said
Must hold it together sort out my head
'There's really no panic, leave him alone
You two go away and leave Chris at home
You'll be fine Chris of this I'm sure'
We stare at each other, gobsmacked once more
'I could stay with my auntie just for a while'
'What a great idea Chris', she gives you a smile
'Have you got 10p? Is she on the phone?
Try to ring now Chris, she can only say no'
You come back looking flushed, 'She say's it's OK'
She hasn't a clue you're in such a bad way
A phone call the next morning, you'd been up all night
Pacing the floor, they knew you weren't right
Paul's getting up now I hear him cough
'I'll get him to Basildon, I can't put this off'
'I don't feel I can cope Paul'
'Then it's best you don't come'
Who can I phone, my sister, my mum?
Paul takes over now he's really quite tough
He looks exhausted he's well had enough
We've been so short-sighted our decision was wrong

We're both feeling weak but we must carry on
'Ring back and tell them I'll pick Christian up
Don't make me tea I'll just throw it up'
They said you resigned yourself to your inevitable plight
You remained very quiet and gave up the fight
I feel very sad now sitting at home
Never before have I felt so alone
The next week just passes, we're both off work
We've never known such unbearable hurt
We sleep endless sleep, slowly rising round 2
Constantly talking and thinking of you
We've done the best thing it's all for the best
This relapse has certainly set us a test

We have never been able to understand why his nurse was saying, 'You two go away for a few days and leave Chris at home.' Of course professionals have to try to keep the situation as calm as possible but this was definitely shutting the gate after the horse had bolted. The very next morning he was admitted to Ward 12. Little did we know that it would be five years before he came home.

Looking back I can see that we should have taken him to hospital on other occasions, but it was fear of the unknown. We managed too well and looking back we can see that we had managed to get him through several mini-relapses. Chris being so totally against going into hospital purely added to the situation. My advice now to carers? Hand things over when you know deep down how bad things are.

When he was admitted to Ward 12, it was made worse by the fact that it was Christmas – usually a very happy time. Then came New Year's Eve when most young people are out having the time of their lives.

Hindsight is a wonderful thing. We should have asked for help sooner; we have all learnt from this. Paul asked to speak to the Ward Manager when he was admitted. He came out of the office and said 'Well we might as well write our son off, from now on I will call schizophrenia "THE ILLNESS OF NO HOPE".' Without hope we are all totally lost. Whatever words professionals use will go round and round the carer's head. If those words are negative, carers will lose hope. If they are positive, you will be keeping hope alive and that will help carers to cope.

After our first visit to Chris on the ward we went straight from the hospital to Basildon town centre to do some shopping. I can remember trying to step onto an escalator and it seemed ages before I was able to do so. Everything felt unreal, we both felt numb. We were exhausted and sleeping until about 2pm and although neither of us was going to work, it seemed as much as we could do to keep the home tidy. We lived on takeaway meals. Even though we'd done everything in our power to try to keep him well, we spent hours talking to him and reassuring him that things would get better, we had failed. I use this next poem a lot during training sessions, it explains exactly what it was like during a crisis.

### WARD 12 BASILDON

I've been here before, just once before
I furtively peep behind the door
One patient sits rocking, another just stares
God I'm so frightened, so very scared
What were you scared of? I hear you say
Never dreamt that my son would be here one day
He's in that cubicle just getting dressed
At this moment he's feeling somewhat depressed
It's to be expected, this is his first stay
I've such a strong urge to take you away
It makes me feel sad as I look at your hair
It stands up on end not that you care
This isn't like you you're usually so smart
God this is really breaking my heart
How are you Chris? I must try to be brave
I'm exhausted mum, and I could do with a shave
Don't worry about that son, I hear your dad say
Back comes the urge to take you away
Away somewhere safe where you're free from pain
An urge we've experienced time and again
It's never been quite this strong before
I worry for Paul – can he take any more?
 I feel so unreal dad – as if I don't exist
We hold your hands and give you a kiss
Your reactions are stunted painfully slow
The nurse comes back in and says, ' Time to go'
Stay home for a few days and get some rest
He's on strong medication, so it's all for the best
So we stay at home for a couple of days
Life passes us by in a kind of haze
We're both feeling numb, it all feels unreal

I worry for Paul as he's looking quite ill
At long last the phone rings on the third day
I've been so very ill mum – I hear you say
I've just lain on my bed, paralysed, stuck
I tried very hard but I couldn't get up
I saw spiders tentacles in Jimmy's head
It all seemed so real I thought he was dead
Jimmy's just fine Chris, he's here with me
Try to calm down, you'll get better you'll see
But they crawled through the walls, the floors and the ceilings
It was terrible mum – you don't know how I'm feeling
Just hang on in there, try your best to be strong
But what's happening mum? It's all going wrong
Benjamin – Chris introduces us to another patient
Mum this is Benjamin – he's unwell too
I'll ask him if he'll sing for you
So Benjamin sang whilst we observed
The loveliest voice we had ever heard
He sang Mary's Boy Child on this bright winter's day
With a voice that could take your breath away
'A long time ago in Bethlehem
So the Holy Bible say
Mary's boy child Jesus Christ
Was born on Christmas Day'
Patients and nurses turned around
Soaking up this beautiful sound
A prolific moment, one I'll never forget
I dare say there's more to experience yet
It's hard to believe it's New Year's Eve
There were no celebrations, all we did was grieve
I'll never forget we all shed a tear
Then told ourselves things would get better next year
Can't bear to think of you over there
Such a strong urge to come stroke your hair
You should be with young people enjoying your time
Not in a psychi ward in bed by 9
Five weeks you were in there time went grindingly slow
We made an appointment to see Dr Lowe
We'll meet on the ward be there by 3
Is Chris allowed home yet? we'll just have to see
As we enter the room we feel the support
We're feeling exhausted emotions are fraught

He shakes our hands and shows us a seat
There's some people here I would like you to meet
Talks and discussions about what to do
We reach an agreement on what's best for you
A rehab centre we've secured him a place
Yet another decision that's so hard to face
By this stage we feel at the end of life's tether
So bathed in support we'll face it together
We reluctantly accept that you're not coming home
At long last we feel that we're not quite so alone

## C. A. R. E: 'COMPASSION AND RESPECT, EDUCATION'

In this day and age a good idea would be regular refresher training sessions to get staff to take stock of how they treat people – nowhere is it needed more than in the 'Caring Professions'. No matter what job we do, we can become complacent but the repercussions have a painful and lasting effect when it comes to nursing of any kind.

In 2006 my 83-year-old mother suffered a stroke. Her neighbour who came in every day to take her dog out, had left her spare set of keys inside the flat the previous day. She looked through the letter box and she could see mum on the floor in the lounge. We had to call the police to break the door down. Paul came home from work and we followed the ambulance in the car.

We were directed to an assessment room. A member of staff said. 'Are you the Shinwell family? Mum's over there.' She was staring and unable to speak, she didn't even recognise me; her mouth had dropped down on one side. We were mortified but no one thought to spare us a few minutes to prepare us and just help to soften the blow.

Although this is about an entirely different situation, I've written this work to highlight the difference that staff attitudes can make. Sister Fiona (Elizabeth Fry Ward) was kindness itself and nothing was too much trouble for her, she took the time to talk to us about our problems at home. I told her about Christian and that my sister was very ill and would not be able to visit. She said to call the ward anytime I needed to; Sister Fiona genuinely cared.

Unfortunately we were about to meet a very different sister. This is exactly what happened.

Two nights before my mum died she said, 'I'd give anything to suck on an ice cube' (she was 'nil by mouth'). We were using little pink sponges to wet the inside of her mouth. Sister Fiona agreed and the nurse wrapped an ice cube in some gauze. Mum said, 'If I had a million pounds I would give it to that nurse for the relief it gave me.' The following night (the night before she died), I asked another nurse for an ice cube and a voice bellowed, 'NOT ON MY WARD!' It was the other sister. She came to the bottom of the bed and said that she would not allow it as mum was aspirating, when I said that she was given one the night before she said, 'That may well be, but this is *my* ward and as I said, not on *my* ward.'

Life was very hard for us. Christian was badly affected by his grandmother being so ill and after she died his medication was almost doubled to help him to cope. I'd spent days sitting by her bed and I was getting ready to go to visit her when the phone rang; unfortunately it wasn't Sister Fiona. 'I think you know what I'm going to say', she said. I said, 'Is it about my mum?' 'Yes', she said, 'she died a few minutes ago.' Although she was of course very ill, we had no idea how close to death she was, in fact I had asked the day before if it would be possible for her to be moved to Thurrock Hospital which is across the road from my home so that I could visit on a regular basis. The nurse said, 'Let's just see how she gets on.'

About 30 minutes later the phone rang again and it was the Sister again. She said, 'Is someone coming over or can we wrap this up?' I had a mental picture of Mum's body being wrapped up. All I can say is if only Sister Fiona had made the phone call, my memories of this painful time would be very different.

### 'SEE ME' (THE CARER)

I'm feeling very tired, I feel anxious and terrified
What will life be without her? What if my mother dies?
What if she doesn't get any better? How will she cope alone?
She so loves her independence, her pets and her comfortable home
What if they say she can't manage and they decide she needs constant care
Will she end up in a complex sat in a high-backed chair?
What will happen to the animals? To lose them would break her heart
How can I deal with all of this, where the hell do I start?
So many worrying questions go round and round in my mind
I need some support and compassion and I need the staff to be kind
So consider how I'm feeling what you see is only a mask
Try to be kind and patient with the many questions I ask
The NHS is understaffed that's crystal clear to see
But I'm worried about my mother so please try your best to see me!!

#### 'SEE ME' (THE PATIENT)

Don't just see my calloused hands or hair a silver sheen
Think about my life gone by and all the things I've been
Don't just see my swollen legs or lines within my face
See a pretty teenager whose life set quite a pace
See a mother to two daughters who loved to buy them things
See a sprightly happy grandma who enjoyed the fun it brings
Don't just see my hearing aid or glasses for my vision
I used to be an officer who made many a decision
Don't just see my walking stick or cold grey walking frame
See me as a person, a person with a name
See me as someone you love even see me as *your* mother
Not just an old and infirm lady, lying here beneath this cover
This will strengthen our relationship, life will seem a little fairer
Treat me as you would your own so that I can see the CARER!!

## BACK TO MENTAL HEALTH

A separate waiting area is needed for those who are suffering from any type of mental distress and their families. Thankfully locally we do have that luxury – a new assessment unit at Basildon Hospital close to where we live. Now for two very different experiences that we had – the first was during a crisis. We were waiting to be seen at the A&E Department at Basildon Hospital and we were greeted by ...

#### A BAD RECEPTIONIST

I wait at the big high desk she doesn't even acknowledge I'm there
She carries on with her paperwork then swivels around in her chair
She answers the telephone, I shuffle from one foot to another
I know I must be polite yet I question should I bother?
She files some patients notes and tidies up the desk
I wonder can she see that I'm feeling distressed
Can I help? She said finally without even looking at me
I need to talk to a member of staff 'well at the moment no one is free
Our staff are all very busy' she said 'Is it urgent or can it wait?'
I can feel my hackles rising like an angry bull at a gate
'It's about my son' I said, she answers the phone yet again
I feel as if I don't exist as well as being a pain
'He's outside with his father he can't cope with being alone'
She totally disregards what I say and answers another phone

'He suffers from schizophrenia' I said, 'it's hard for him to wait in here'
'He'll have to take his turn' she said her tone is sharp, 'Is that clear?'
'Do you think we'll have to wait long?' I said 'My son's in quite a state'
I can feel my hackles rising again I'll be losing my rag at this rate
I read a note pinned to the desk ' STAFF WON'T TOLERATE BAD
   BEHAVIOUR'
I smile to myself in silence experiencing some of the flavour
'Can you wait over there?' She said 'You're standing in the way'
I control myself and say nothing, there's nothing left to say
Front-line staff are so important they speak for the NHS
Manners, compassion and kindness make a good receptionist

But on another occasion we met:

### A GOOD RECEPTIONIST
'Can I help you?' she said – immediate eye contact this time
'I need to speak to a member of staff', 'I understand dear, that's fine
I'll try to sort it out for you' she ignores the ring of the phone
Her attitude is so different I don't feel the need to moan
She's warm and understanding, compassionate and kind
I'm feeling so much calmer and beginning to unwind
'It's really busy' she said, 'It could be quite a wait'
I find that I don't feel angry, I don't get myself in a state
'That's absolutely fine' I said 'I understand how things are'
There's no bad feeling between us, I don't feel we're fighting a war
'I'll wait over here' I said 'I'll get out from under your feet'
An excellent receptionist what a pleasure you are to meet

And yet again, this nurse was wearing her 'ever so professional hat'. Carers make many phone calls to the wards, this is about one I won't forget in a hurry:

### MORE TO GAIN
Who is your son? She enquired in a brisk and clinical tone
His name is Christian Wakefield I said to this voice at the end of the phone
You've already called us earlier today!! I almost ask who's counting?
I can feel myself losing my cool I can feel my temper mounting
Things are just the same, you're aware that your son is quite poorly
Would a little compassion be too much to ask?
The answer to that is surely
We will call you if things change but there's no need to keep ringing us
I feel like a scolded five-year-old, am I making too much fuss?

Now try to imagine it's your son, how would you like to be greeted?
With manners, with kindness, professionally, that's how you should be
    treated

I thought it might be helpful to write something about how I was feeling at the time. When I conduct talks, I always ask the staff to remember that before a carer actually gets to see a member of staff, they have probably been to hell and back

### 'SEE ME' (THE CARER)

I'm feeling so very stressed, anxious, exhausted and tense
What if he doesn't get better? This relapse doesn't make sense
What if they send him home, how on earth will we cope this time?
How much more can we take, we're nearing the end of the line
It's been seven long years of struggling, seven long years of hell
Were still grieving for our son, the son we knew so well
So many worrying questions go round and round in my mind
I need support and compassion and I need the staff to be kind

# 9

# You Can't Leave Me Here!

### WEYMARKS

After five weeks on the acute ward and on heavy medication Chris was moved to a rehab centre, manned by fully trained nurses 24/7. We would visit on Wednesday evenings and we usually tried to take him out for a ride in the car. Very often, he was so confused, anxious and thought disordered that we'd go around the nearest roundabout and take him back for yet another chat with one of the nurses – some of them not much older than him. Most of the other patients were older than him. One elderly lady, who had been in the system for years, thought she was pregnant. I can vividly remember a day during the summer when she was telling everyone that the baby was due soon. One of the other patients was wearing an overcoat even though it was sweltering and even though he was sweating profusely which created a pungent smell that filled the air. Chris looked so young and handsome, it broke my heart to leave him there but I knew that we didn't have a choice.

This poem describes the desperate phone calls we received from him on a regular basis. We ended up feeling sad and frustrated that we couldn't help him and words felt so inadequate. As bizarre as it all seems to us, to him of course it is very real. We can't even imagine what it must be like when it feels as if everybody is plotting against you or talking about you. This includes TV, radio, staff, family and even people going past in their cars.

DESPERATE PHONE CALLS

Desperate phone calls and you're frantic again
You run on and you're in so much pain
Don't leave me here Mum, let me come home
Can you hear them saying things over the phone?
Paul and Sid are as bad, they do it too
How on earth can I help you to see it's not true?

Last Sunday Chris, you accused me of the same
Then why do I hear them saying my name?
I know that it's pointless when you start to cry
Listen to me Mum you know I don't lie
I'm not sleeping well, I keep pacing the floor
Please come and get me, I can't take any more
Mum why's this world so cruel to me
How do I reply? Can YOU tell me?
Go and speak to the staff Chris, they'll listen to you
I don't see the point Mum, be honest do you?
I put the phone down knowing you're still in pain
Desperate phone calls again and again
I contact your nurse who says with a frown
Just refer him to us and put the phone down
I want to escape, but there's nowhere to run
It's not quite that easy when it's your son

## WRITING IS VERY CATHARTIC

Time to explain how the floodgates opened to my writing and how helpful it's been. One day my sister rang and asked Paul and me to go with her and Colin (her husband), to King's College in Cambridge. I reluctantly agreed. As we walked through the college, a lady approached us and pointed to a small chapel where people could go to pray. I said, 'I don't believe there's a God after what has happened to my son.' My sister insisted that I go with her as she wanted to say a prayer. She prayed for me and for Christian and I didn't give this a lot more thought. At 2am the following morning I woke up and my mind was consumed with words. It wasn't possible to ignore the compulsion to write. The words began with 'Nine long years have been and gone are we any further on?' They flowed and flowed and it was totally effortless it felt as if my hand was being guided over the pages. I still have piles of old cards with writing on. I'd write on anything that I could lay my hands on. It was always strongest during the night and I would creep around so as not to wake Paul up, although he did wake up occasionally. He kept telling me that he was worried that I was becoming manic again.

My family were very concerned and like Paul they thought I was becoming unwell again, Paul kept saying, 'You're going high, you have to stop this.' Hard as I tried I couldn't get them to see that writing was making me feel better, not worse. Some nights I'd wake up at 2am, write until 5am, get back into bed and sleep till 7am and then effortlessly I'd get up and go to work.

This is about the most difficult weekend we ever had. We'd picked Chris up on Friday evening for his weekend stay with us but we soon realised that he was far too unwell to stay at home. He kept asking Paul, 'Are you really my dad?' Paul ran down the garden and I found him sobbing behind the shed. Chris's thoughts were so disjointed that he was saying 'I'm a which one what' or 'Am I a got?' So what was he thinking, he was speaking but nothing made any sense at all. He believed that the television, the stereo and even people outside in cars were talking about him. He rang to speak to Ash (his nurse) several times and normally after talking things through, he'd calm down but this time nothing seemed to work. He seemed to think that because he'd experienced me being ill, that the symptoms were the same and that's why he was forever asking me whether I used to see things, he got angry when I said no. The poem also describes how much he relied on the staff for constant reassurance.

#### MUM DO YOU THINK I'LL EVER BE FREE?

You stare back at me so searchingly
Mum do you think I'll ever be free?
I'm sick of this world, I can't cope with this life
Tired of the worry, isolation and strife
Do you think I'm evil? Do you think I'm good?
I can't seem to find myself, if only I could
I see dreadful things every new day
And why won't the voices go away?
Still visions appear in front of me
Mum do you think I'll ever be free?
It's as if I'm reliving such evil dreams
I repeat to myself that it's not what it seems
Yes Mum I know that I must be strong
I get too many thoughts surely that's wrong
They fight in my mind for supremacy
Mum do you think I'll ever be free?
My thoughts come so fast it all feels so wrong
Then my mind's blank the thoughts are all gone
The thoughts don't make sense like I'm a which what one
Yes I'll ring Weymarks they'll help me Mum
They help me to see that none of it's real
They're so understanding they know how I feel

Is that you Ash? I'm not doing well
Hallucinations and voices are giving me hell
I try to see that none of it's true
But how would you cope if it happened to you?
Yes I'll try harder thanks for sorting it out
You've helped me to see what it's all about
I feel much better now Ash is so good
I knew that he'd help me I told you he would
TEN MINUTES LATER
Turn off the TV Mum they keep on at me
They know what I'm thinking they steal thoughts you see
Sometimes I can even pick up on theirs too
When you were ill did this happen to you?
I'll turn off my stereo, they do it too
When you were ill did this happen to you?
They make me confused and I can't work things out
How on earth can they tell what I'm thinking about?
Don't try to trick me I know that it's true
Why don't you admit that it happened to you?
Why do you lie Mum? That's really unfair
I don't know why you pretend that you care
If you really cared then you'd own up to me
Mum do you think that I'll ever be free?
It's so hard to remember who I really am
Will I find myself? Do you think that I can?
I try so hard Mum, really I do
What did they say, did you hear that too?
Why do they tease me? I can't take much more
They keep me awake at night pacing the floor
I try to work out why it's happened to me
Mum do you think I'll ever be free?
You had illness Mum, How did you cope?
How on earth did you manage to hang on to hope?
Nine years of my life now that's far too long
Do you think there's much longer for me to hold on?
It makes me feel dirty, disgusting and bad
It makes me feel angry, frustrated and sad
You look very tired Dad and so does Mum
Tell me the truth, Am I really your son?
You're cunning though Mum, so cunning and sly
Oh don't be pathetic there's no need to cry
I feel agitated it's so hard to sit still

Why do I worry that my brother's ill?
What's that they said I'm a which one what
They either said that or I'm only a got
I'll ring Ash again I must try to stay strong
What's happening Mum, it's all gone wrong?
I'm scared that I will see spiders again
It's all so unfair to be in this pain
It's me again Ash, I'm mentally unwell
Seeing and hearing things, God it's been hell
My parents are fine, no I'm not coming back
Help me get out of this Ash, there must be a knack
Of course there's a knack Ash, there must be a key
For God's sake Ash, please tell me
You're staring again, this time pleadingly
Mum do you think I'll ever be free?
I'm stuck in it again and I can't move on
Is dad walking the dog? Am I really his son?
I'll close this one now I could go on and on
A typical weekend endured by my son
So what do you think? You tell me
Do you think my son will ever be free?

During difficult times there are still things that can make us smile. When Chris was in rehab he went out one evening with a fellow patient who was around the same age as him. They went for a drink in town, an extremely rare occurrence. They got talking to two girls and in Christian's words, 'I wanted the ground to open up when Richard said, 'Allow me to introduce us, I'm Richard and this is Christian and we're both paranoid schizophrenics.' I know it must have been hard for Chris but I had to say what I was thinking and that was – 10 out of 10 for guts! Richard had well and truly gone past the stage of hiding it or being totally embarrassed by it. When Chris said to Richard 'How could you?' He replied 'It's their problem – they should take the time to learn a bit more about mental illness.'

## RETHINK MENTAL HEALTH CONFERENCE ON 1ST JULY, 1999

Chris has been in rehab now for two years, he is 25 years old. Paul and I went to a mental health conference (and thank God we did). Dr R, a professor of psychiatry (since retired) from the Maudsley Hospital in London was on the stage talking to the audience.

During the break I called her and told her about Christian. Her first question was 'Have they tried clozapine?' to which I replied, 'No, doctor.' She said it was the best drug for treatment resistant schizophrenia (TRS). She said to go back and ask for a trial for Chris (if he agreed). I said 'But surely they must know it wouldn't work for him?' and she replied, 'How can they possibly know without trying it?' When I told her that I had asked the GP for a referral a long time ago and he'd refused saying 'I have a letter here which states it wouldn't matter where you took your son' she went on to say, 'If your son had a brain tumour, they would have referred him. They wouldn't have refused him a second opinion, that's happened because he suffers from schizophrenia.' It just shows how green we were, we'd just accepted what the GP had said and gone home and forgotten it. This makes me feel as if I didn't do enough but at the time I was very weak myself. But I will always wonder was there more we could have done, had we been stronger? It has taught me a very big lesson and that is to find out about your rights. Don't just accept what you are told, don't be intimidated just because you feel that these people know best.

Dr R gave me her direct line number (a privilege I've never had before) and told me to contact her if we had problems and she would make sure that Chris was given a trial on clozapine. I have written and spoken to her since to keep her in touch with what's going on.

## DR D AND THE COOK REPORT

I went to see Dr D on August 10th 1999 at 9.30am at Basildon Hospital, Ward 12. When we got there his Registrar apologised and said that Dr D's secretary had forgotten to put our appointment in the diary. He went on to say that he knew why we'd asked for the appointment – it was because we'd heard about clozapine. He took us into a private room and explained clozapine to us in detail. He said that Dr D agreed to try Chris on it if (of course) Christian agreed to a change of medication. He said we had one week to think about it and that Dr D would see us all at Weymarks on Wednesday 18th August at 3pm. He said that in the meantime he would go to Weymarks and go through Christian's notes and when Christian came home for the weekend, we could ask him if he was willing to try it.

Stephen took time off work to come with us. When we got to

Weymarks, Chris was already in consultation with Dr D. They finally joined us but Chris seemed angry. He said Dr D had said that he wasn't trying hard enough, yet Ash had told us only the week before that they were very pleased with him and that he had completed his care plan successfully.

We went into to see Dr D; also in the room was a CPN and a social worker. He started talking about Chris not trying hard enough. After about 10 minutes I said that Christian was happy to give clozapine a try. He didn't seem to know what we were talking about. He said he had no intention of trying it and that he was putting him on amisulpiride for six months. We were shocked and we just looked at each other. We explained what Dr Phillip had said (take a week to think about it) but he still didn't appear to know what we were talking about. I showed him a note from my son to Dr Lowe (written Jan 1$^{st}$ 1995). It showed how desperate Chris was to get better. I said, 'Does this sound like someone who does not want to get well?' Stephen plucked up some courage and asked him, 'Is it because these drugs are more expensive than others?' 'No', he said, 'And I'm not willing to discuss this any further, I'm the consultant and I've made my decision.' We could see that there was no point in arguing with him and by this stage, although disappointed, we were grateful for a change in medication.

A few nights later we were watching TV and a programme called 'The Cook Report' came on which exposes people. The title of this edition was 'Doctors From Hell'. There was Dr D being chased around a psychiatric ward by Roger Cook and his team. They were questioning him about sexually molesting his own patients. Needless to say we had very little sleep. A helpline for relatives and patients was set up and I was given an appointment for 3pm Wednesday 25$^{th}$ August. I felt very sorry for the ward manager as he had to do all the explaining and consequently take all the aggravation from angry carers.

I explained that I wasn't there because I had any concern that Dr D had done anything untoward to my son, but I was concerned that when we saw him in Wednesday 18$^{th}$ August, he did not seem to know what we were talking about, even though he'd promised to put him on clozapine if Chris agreed. The outcome was that Christian was put on clozapine days later. In a way this worked in our favour. I insisted on a letter of apology for Christian as he was very distressed by all this. I felt that this was the very least they could do. And of course as the story goes on you will see that this drug had very good results. In fact we could see a difference within days.

If you read this story to the end, you will see that I wrote to 'The Sun' newspaper as I find it very hard to believe that they have the audacity to call people who suffer from mental illness 'Sickos, Psychos, Schizos, Nutters' and yet in the newspaper report on Dr D he is given respect and referred to as a doctor.

Chris was put on clozapine on Monday 20th September 1999 and we feel that this is where his story changes; we believe that it was only then that he slowly began to recover. The worst part for us was the betrayal. Dr D was in the ultimate position of trust and he abused it. So many people were affected by his actions. But this was not as bad as the effect it had on Christian. Due to the nature of his illness and the fact that he went to woodwork classes, etc, everyone was naturally talking about it. Christian thought that people were talking about him. He rang several times saying that the police were after him and that he'd done something terrible sexually to someone. It was very hard to pacify him, his paranoia increased a lot at this time. I think what made it worse was that I liked Dr D. I can remember him asking Chris if there was anything about Weymarks that he would like to change. To which Chris replied, 'I wish that the others were around my age.' To which Dr D replied, Oh, we've got all that in hand, we're giving all the others an injection tonight and by this time tomorrow they will all be 24 just like you.' He was sentenced to 18 months' imprisonment ...

# 10

# Clozapine:
# A breakthrough

Christian agreed to try this new drug. We were very proud of him because ever since he experienced the dystonic reaction he'd been terrified that if they changed his medication, it could happen again.

Even though we knew that this drug might not work, there was always a chance that it would and we desperately needed that glimmer of hope. Leading up to the clozapine trial he had been very unwell. We think he took this chance because he was so very sick of being ill; I think he would have agreed to almost anything.

We were in a state of shock each time we went to see him as he seemed even better than the time before. I suppose the only people who can really appreciate this are families who are going through the same thing and of course the staff who see them every day. They too were pleased with his progress. The thing that worries me is there are still people out there who are not getting the best medication. Some carers go for years without even knowing about treatment resistant schizophrenia or that clozapine is the gold standard. Some carers, for various reasons, either abandon their loved ones or give up the fight. In all honesty I can understand this. I have been blessed with a very supportive family. Others are not so fortunate, and I can't honestly say hand on heart that I would have coped without the support that I have had. Mothers are hard-wired to make things better but sometimes we have to accept that there is nothing we can do, other than love them.

Written at 4am on 15th November 1999. How can you explain last weekend? It is almost impossible. If we'd won the lottery it could not have come even close to the feeling of elation. I am not saying it was all plain sailing, but the confusion was gradually lifting. For years we have said how lovely it would be to hold a conversation with our son, and we did. It was a very strange experience. If it felt like that to us, it is hard to imagine what it was like for Christian. We went to see him after a few days on clozapine and we were already able to see a change taking place. All we can do now is pray that things continue to improve.

### THE SEEDS OF RECOVERY

The seeds of sweet recovery
Take root after endless eternity
Growing stronger after so many years
Watered daily by many tears
Growth that finally provides the key
Unlocking the seeds of recovery.
Tend the rich soil with tired hands
Reap the new harvest and keep making plans
Seeds we planted so long ago
Fed faithfully with love to watch them grow
With hope replenished you make your way
At last looking forward to the next day
No more endless sleep or angry voices
Far less confused and making choices
Gone evil dreams and hallucinations
Far more relaxed without these frustrations
Rich and nourishing cool dark earth
Encouraging growth and promoting rebirth
So good to see you less paranoid
In a far kinder world and filling the void
Rebuilding your life a mammoth task
'Where do I begin?' you quietly ask
At the beginning I gently suggest
Don't take on too much, take time to rest
Tread oh so lightly one step at a time
Remember you walk a very fine line
Tend the rich soil and at last we can see
Seeds of sweet recovery

## FELLOW SUFFERERS

I'd like to tell you about some other families I have met along the way. I have asked their permission of course. No names will be used.

One lady took her son to hospital in sheer desperation. He began drinking to drown the voices. He would sometimes smoke two cigarettes at a time and stub them out on his mattress. She couldn't sleep because he was ranting and raving all night. One Sunday morning she took him to hospital to be told, 'Take him home, we haven't got a bed for him.'

Another young man became so ill that he stabbed someone because he firmly believed that this person was living inside his own skin. His parents were told that he was one of the worst cases they had seen. The only drug that in 11 years managed to control his symptoms is clozapine. He has been stable on it for a number of years, but tragically he and his family will pay a high price for the rest of their lives for that fact that this young man became so very ill, which led to such dreadful consequences.

Yet another mother that I speak to on a regular basis is terrified that her 28-year-old son will eventually kill himself. He believes that he is Elvis Presley's son and that there are people trying to kill him, in his words, 'as they killed my father'. This lady doesn't know where to turn and in the back of my mind I'm constantly wondering would clozapine help him? I think of the other lad and I hear his mother saying, 'He was the worst case of psychosis they'd seen and now look at him, stable at long last.'

I am well aware that there is no cure for schizophrenia. I have also finally accepted that my son will never be as well as he would have been or achieve what he might have done but hopefully, readers will see that he doesn't go through that hell anymore and we often say that over the years, we have wondered if the life he had was really worth living. Christian's quality of life has changed dramatically for the better and we no longer feel terrified of what we might have to go through next.

In conclusion, these are the questions I constantly ask myself. Why in the name of God does it keep going on? Why are people still dying, either through suicide or the desperate actions of a very sick person? Will I ever be able to mention that word schizophrenia without seeing that look I all too often get? A mixture of horror and lack of understanding rolled into one. If and when I ever get an answer to these questions I will be able to rest.

Chris sometimes stares at me in amazement when I'm doing the housework; he says, 'Mum, how do you and dad keep working without getting tired?' I only work a few hours but I feel so very tired.' He does get better as the day goes on (as we all do), but the first thing I notice when he gets up, irrespective of the time, is the tiredness. I suppose it's like everything else, he's become used to it after 20 years.

## KITKATTS ROAD, CANVEY ISLAND

And so after about 12 weeks on clozapine and two-and-a-half years in 24 hour care, it was time to leave Weymarks and say goodbye to the people who had cared for him, including the other clients.

Getting Chris ready for independent living was a very gradual process and this time he'd be living in 12 hour care for another two-and-a-half years.

Once again I have to say the staff were extremely good at Kitkatts Road. I went to pick him up from Weymarks and settle him into another new home. Saying goodbye to Sid, Des and Paul was very hard for Christian.

THEIR VOICE

I've been a silent witness
For far too many years
I've met many other sufferers
Cried many futile tears
Not just for my own son
But for the others he has known
As I watched them battle bravely
My respect for them has grown
I've sat in rehab centres
I've watched them shuffle past
I've prayed to God that one day
They'll find some peace at last
There must be some way I could help them
It seemed ludicrous to me
I've marvelled at their strength
Their sheer tenacity
Embedded in my memory are Sid and Des and Paul
Many more that I could mention
I respect them one and all
Along with dedicated nurses who've listened endlessly
To irrational fears and worries
So very patiently
For years I felt so helpless
Was there nothing I could do?
Then a miracle occurred
And the writing filtered through
I thank God I started writing

It's given me a choice
No more a silent witness
I'll try to be their voice


## IGNORANCE

I can remember taking Chris for his injection at Sunnyside when he was about 18 and I was talking to a lady who was with her daughter. I said, 'Is this your daughter?' as if the poor girl didn't exist. I often cringe when I think of how they must have felt.

I was no different from the people who stare at me blankly when I talk about Christian. I know that (with the knowledge I have now) I would be angry if somebody did it to me. Once someone asked if my son was a schizophrenic and I replied, 'No, my son is a young man who suffers from a condition they call schizophrenia.'

At Kitkatts, Chris had an excellent CPN – Lydia Chalk, who was totally dedicated and supported Paul and me too. Lydia made us feel part of things rather than enemies to be avoided at all costs. A further two-and-a-half years eventually passed ... And so at last it was time for Chris to come home. We sometimes wondered if he would have to stay in care indefinitely.

This brings us to the end of my first book 'Schizophrenia – A Mother's Story' and the beginning of 'Schizophrenia Through The Maze'. With Steve's help we furnished the flat and, although we were relieved that he was coming home, as always our feelings were mixed with fear and trepidation, not knowing how he would cope. Time for us to go ...

# 11

# Through the Maze

**THROUGH THE MAZE**
Are words really adequate?
Will words help me to explain
What this journey is really like
Through understanding there's much to be gained
Standing here at the entrance
To a maze that's daunting and long
Will we find our way to the exit?
Will we manage somehow to stay strong?
Will words help us to cope on our journey?
Help the reader to understand?
Will words help us to support each other
So that empathy goes hand in hand?
But words are all that I have
Along with memories we'll need to erase
Readers join us till the end of our journey
Through schizophrenia's maze

What do they say? We never know what's around the corner and it's just as well we don't sometimes – was Christian back in the community? Or was he out in the backwaters? What we were totally unprepared for was twofold, firstly STIGMA and secondly, after five years of being in care, it was a case of the sole responsibility of caring once again laid firmly at our door. Similar to the wilderness years, life for all of us became extremely painful and difficult. Yet again we were witnessing the isolation slowly destroying him and once again we were all living in fear of another relapse!

He'd come round every day at about 10am with nowhere to go and nothing to do. As he sat staring out of the window, sometimes for hours on end, he would say, 'What are all of these people doing Mum, where are they all going?' But there was nothing I could do about it apart from say, 'Things will get better, you will start to pick up the pieces.' Winter is always far worse. We all feel uplifted when the sun shines; long cold dark winter months purely make life harder. We racked our brains to try to find him things to do. He joined a club (2 hours weekly), a few miles away. Each time I dropped him off, I would cry all the way home.

Sometimes he'd come to see me but only stay for about ten minutes saying that he didn't feel comfortable. He told me that he didn't feel comfortable anywhere. He'd go back to his flat and straight away he felt lonely, so back he'd come again. When I asked him what it felt like he'd say, 'It's like being on a pinball table and going backwards and forwards or standing on a kerb and not knowing whether or not to step off of the kerb or stay on it.' An extremely painful place to be ...

ISOLATION AND PINBALL GAMES

I'm engulfed by isolation, I'm sick of the loneliness
I'm aware that there's a world out there
Which makes me more depressed
I watch it go by from my window
People with normal lives
They don't rely on their ageing parents
As a way to exist or survive
They hurry past my window
They don't even know that I'm here
It feels like my spirit is shrinking
Yet another salty tear
I try hard to feel comfortable
I rush from here to there
But no matter where I am
I'm gripped by agony and despair
It's like I'm the ball in a pinball game
Shunted from here to there
I end up feeling so depressed
And thinking life's so unfair
I reflect on when life was so different
Before I got hit by this curse
Before the antipsychotics, consultants, rehab, a nurse
I'm safe in my lonely cocoon, but it's hard to explain the frustration
Schizophrenia has stolen my youth
And replaced it with isolation

## TREATING THE WHOLE FAMILY

The months passed and one morning I was conducting a talk locally. At the end a lady gave me a telephone number, she asked was Chris having any talking therapy and that it might help if I rang this doctor for advice.

This was how we came to meet Dr. Dianne Lefevre and she suggested a unique talking therapy for Christian. In our ignorance during his stay at Kitkatts, we had taken him for five sessions with a CBT counsellor (privately) at the cost of £30 an hour. Eventually he refused to go. We didn't realise that he needed to be assessed to find out which therapy would suit him best. Because Chris has problems with controlling his thoughts, CBT purely added to his frustration.

Christian had an appointment with Dianne at Basildon Hospital. She used to head the Psychotherapy Department, but has since retired. She asked me to sit in on part of the three-hour assessment. I'll never forget the look of amazement on his face. It was as if he was thinking, 'At last someone understands, someone is explaining this to me and it makes far more sense to me now.' During the therapy there is an attempt to empower the non-psychotic process (or healthy self) and this erodes the influence of the psychotic process or the 'other mind' (TOM).

The therapy (the concept of the 'other mind') is combined with art therapy – the sessions lasted for one-and-a-half hours weekly and Chris attended them for three-and-a-half years. This time it was different; he didn't object to going and even though he was very confused, especially at the beginning, he seemed to know that the therapy was helping.

During all of the early years, I've lost count of the times that Chris and I have looked at each other in desperation. 'Why can't I understand what's happening to me? Why doesn't someone explain why my life is so difficult?' Or from my perspective, 'What the hell is happening to my son? There must be someone who can explain this illness to me; I feel totally confused!'

The 'other mind' is destructive and often comes into play if someone is trying to get too close. Some people seem to find it difficult to understand this. Since I have learned the concept of the 'other mind', I have been pulled up by both carers and professionals who have said that using the term the 'other mind' implies that the person has a split personality, when in actual fact it's about being able to see that we all live in two minds whether we have a mental illness or not. To understand this more clearly, read Chapter 12 as Dianne has written this herself (A Balanced Approach). To me it makes perfect sense and I can say in all honesty that it has helped all of us. Instead of all of us going round and round in circles, we all have something to work with. In all of these years, he has never talked openly about his symptoms. Now, when his thoughts are bothering him, he will talk to me, Paul and even Stephen.

Dianne's work offers patients and families far more than just medication. She explained that Christian's problems probably began before he could even speak and that chronic psychosis is often associated with ADHD in childhood. During the interview, we discussed how Christian's behaviour could have been down to his having developed ADHD, which had obviously gone unnoticed. This made so much sense to me and none of what she said came as any surprise. In fact this new-found knowledge has also helped Paul and me to come to terms with things. I can see now that it was there waiting in the wings all of the time, I am able to see that he was definitely predisposed to psychosis, but therapy is about understanding, whereas blaming is both unhelpful and destructive.

Teachers need to be trained on what to look out for so that they can alert parents. Surely, seeing the early warning signs will help a great deal and youngsters could be given EPA in omega-3 fats for a start. There should be far more research into early infancy and childhood and finding ways to recognise these traits and possibly prevent them from developing into a full-blown psychosis later in life – yet again, prevention is better than cure. If you take into consideration the costs, both in emotional turmoil and money – being able to recognise early warning signs and act on them has to be the way forward.

Dianne suggested family therapy to help prise Christian and me apart. She also set up a carers' group which I attended for three years, along with five other carers. This has all helped immensely.

Dr Dianne Lefevre is a consultant psychiatrist in psychotherapy, BCP registered, psychoanalytical psychotherapist and Hon. Fellow APU. She says, 'With serious mental illness I believe there can be no single approach to what is a multi-system illness, we are attempting to set up carers' groups where topics such as the benefits of taking omega-3 fats, combined with psychotherapeutically working with the "other mind".

'In the group it can be discussed, along with the other facets of a multi-pronged treatment. It's a huge burden off carers' shoulders when they discover that the person that they care for functions as if they are two people and that can take the sting out of some of the more hurtful and aggressive interchanges that can be so exhausting for all concerned.'

Professor William MacFarlane from the USA has researched the benefits of psychoeducation in multi-family groups and has found that it has had very positive effects on both sufferers and their carers. This is very impressive news about the effectiveness of such an approach.

Paul and I are witnessing the improvements every day. Take last night – we were all getting ready to go out for the evening. Steve and Angela were coming too. Chris had a wash and put his suit on, but he became very agitated and said that even though he had washed himself something was telling him to go and do it again, and that he still felt dirty. We said, 'The "other mind" is telling you that.' He said, 'Yes I know it is and I'm not going to take any notice of it'. Obviously, sometimes it's not as easy as that, but at least he is working with it. Please note that patients have to reach a certain level of recovery to engage in this therapy.

We were lucky enough to meet a doctor who believed that the treatment of psychosis is about delivering a balanced approach, not just medication and a four-weekly visit from a practitioner ...

# A Balanced Approach*

## Dr Dianne LeFevre

Most of what is written about caring for and suffering from mental illness and pain is from the point of view of psychiatrists, neurobiologists, psychotherapists and other professionals. It is not a balanced view. It is difficult for professionals to take the risk of seeing 'it' from the other side. It is too threatening, perhaps because we can all so easily cross the line.

In the mid 80s I was lucky to work with Frank Morrison, who was unafraid, a wonderful man and a wonderful teacher. He came from a nursing background and was the project manager of the Hawthorn Project. The Hawthorn Project included a nurse training facility attached to a group psychotherapy project/therapeutic community for people who had been in hospital with chronic psychoses for 8 to 60 years! Frank showed me how to learn from our patients who had endured unimaginable suffering both from the illness and from us, the professionals. The patients were the best teachers.

It was at that time, when I was working as a psychiatrist, that a young man who had recovered from a severe psychotic illness came to the outpatient clinic. He grinned as he sat down. ' What is the difference between God and a psychiatrist?' he said.

'Go on tell me.'

'God knows he is not a psychiatrist.'

We both had a good laugh. I have used the joke at many of the talks that I have given and in lectures on the meaning of jokes and the pathology of practitioners. The joke could equally apply to all medical practitioners, psychotherapists, mental health practitioners, and so on. It has a serious side, as do most jokes.

Every day I meet carers or sufferers who are quietly or loudly desperate about their situation. They often have horror stories to

* Previously published in *Schizophrenia Through the Maze and Fighting Back: A book for carers* by Georgina Wakefield. Academic Press.

tell about the indignities, neglect, misunderstandings they have suffered at the hands of professionals – often well-meaning professionals and sometimes people who have been rendered callous and insensitive by ambition, grandiosity, an inability to tolerate failure or the crippling demands of the understaffed NHS, which is, at this time (2006 to 2010), rife with bullying, power abuse and misinformation. In Trusts crippled by poor morale, senior staff will look you in the eye and tell you how proud they are of the excellent morale in the workplace. Poor morale amongst staff always reflects upon patient care, which deteriorates as a result. Unacknowledged, it cannot be put right.

Forays into manic grandiosity are part of the human condition. So even well-meaning professionals resort to a secret grandiosity: 'Of course I know best, and I am the best in the business.' Sometimes it is not a secret. I was told recently of a practitioner, who said, absolutely seriously, to his patient: 'If I were modest I would say I am the best psychiatrist in the county. In fact I am one of the best in the country.'

We professionals have to learn to look at our own pathology and ourselves. We need to start by being more tolerant of our own failings and weaknesses so that we can get down to the business of listening to the people we are supposed to be treating, people whose suffering plumbs depths that are – I was about to write unimaginable but the problem is that they *are* probably imaginable although the imagination is reigned in out of fear. This suffering, which can be intolerable, includes the people who have illnesses and those caring for them.

The manic grandiosity that is so prevalent among the caring professionals can probably be understood as a defence against helplessness, the frustration of being unable to understand what is going on and the fear of being unable to come up with the 'cure' and of being unable to relieve the symptoms. However, I think we are now at a stage where many carers and sufferers would prefer to know that the practitioner has doubts and does not/cannot know the answers and cannot cure. Doctors don't 'cure'. They help the body to heal itself.

A more realistic attitude would be creative. The idea that the sufferer, the carer, the professional are working and *thinking together* can be developed. It could fruitfully be a case of: 'Let us think and work together to try and deal with this extraordinarily painful disruptive situation. If thinking is not possible for you at this particular time, then those who can think and act will try and take over for the time being until you are able to do so.'

For years we have been getting things wrong about illness and in particular mental illness. There is an idea that, rather like an event horizon on the edge of a black hole, there is a point beyond which an individual falls into the hole and becomes labelled with a severe mental illness, and after this ... mayhem? Well, at this point professionals take over, often offering contradictory views and not always offering the help that is needed or wanted. The horrors of stigmatisation have to be suffered and so it is often downhill from there onwards for sufferer and, if present, carers. I would stress that this is not *always* the case but it is so all too often.

Actually the world is not divided into the mad and the not-mad. We all travel up and down a spoke which has, at one end, relatively healthy functioning and at the other, great difficulty in functioning at all. Quite a lot of us never reach a point where a diagnosis is made. But far too many do. My impression is that there are more people concealing symptoms out of fear than we realise.

Some ill individuals can travel back to healthy functioning. For reasons that are not well understood, some people fail to return to the state of relative health. Georgie Wakefield, with her amazing energy and enthusiasm, is doing pioneering work for carers. Her book is mainly concerned with the carers of those who get stuck in a mental illness and have great difficulty in travelling back along the spoke to relatively easy, pain-free functioning.

## USEFUL QUESTIONS

The questions that it might be useful to tackle in this chapter are as follows:

1. Can people designated 'well' have some idea about what it is like to be trapped in a psychotic process called a mental illness?

2. How do we understand the fact that an individual attempting to cut his throat may on the one hand say: 'I am Hitler and people are coming to punish me for my crimes – I have to kill myself', while ten minutes later the same individual may be inquiring when his next therapy session is and worrying about perfectly ordinary things, such as whether he has enough money for the laundrette. It is as if two people are functioning in the same body. This is working in two minds. What is this 'two minds' idea about and what is its purpose?

3. How do we understand in developmental terms the situation where an individual is entrapped in the 'other mind' – the psychotic process?

4. Where do omega-3 fatty acids come in?

5. Why is shame so important?

6. What can we do about this state of affairs? Is there a management strategy that can be helpful?

*1. So first, can we have some idea about what it is like to be trapped in a psychotic process called a mental illness?*

I believe that everyone functions using two minds – a healthy self and another mind that pulls one away from creative relationships. So I think we can have an idea of what it is like. Try this as an exercise.

Imagine that you have in error, when tired, said something really hurtful to someone you like and admire, somebody by whom you wish to be liked. You go away and your mind goes round and round in the following way: you think to yourself: 'Why on earth did I say that, I am a total idiot, what am I going to do. Why on earth did he have to turn up just when I was feeling tired. Couldn't he have stayed at home, then it would not have happened.'

You go on attacking your tired self that has made an error and attacking the person who took the brunt of your insensitivity. You wake up at 2am and the same thoughts go round and round. You can't stop thinking them. You can't sleep. It is akin to being in a dream-like state from which you cannot escape. The thinking you employ is called calculative thinking, stimulated by the wish to escape from the potential shame involved within the situation rather than to think creatively about it. What happens is that you repetitively attack yourself and the person who turned up to try to justify the gaff. It does not work. You become incapable of opening your mind in a fully alert state to the facts of the matter.

If you have a relatively strong healthy self, you will go to a friend and tell them about how you put your foot in it. Any sensible friend would say something like: 'For heaven's sake, you have not killed anyone. Go and apologise and put it right.' With help you begin to think creatively. You establish contact with the person, apologise and more often than not all is resolved and the tormenting thoughts go away.

If however, the incident was not so trivial and occurred

repeatedly and there were a number of added ingredients, other crucial factors such as the episode occurring at a very young age in the presence of a healthy but unformed self and persisting for a long time, it could spin off and – as it were – become fuel for the development and enlargement of the other mind, the psychotic process, the germ of which is in all of us. It could then take on a life of its own, expand and become established as a psychotic illness.

You can see that the preoccupation about your gaff could become a suffocating, inescapable dream-world that could occupy all your thoughts and haul you away from the outside world in which you feel awake. Imagine what that might be like.

When you are able to experiment with what I have just said, you will realise that there is something addictive about being in these states. You quite often don't want them to be interrupted and if you are interrupted, the minute the interruption ceases you go back to the same thoughts. Thus it is sometimes more tolerable to continue being preoccupied in a circle of psychotic thoughts and ideas, in this dream-like state, rather than to return to the day's humdrum activities.

Patients with whom I have discussed this phenomenon can identify with it. For those who live with people who are at the time overwhelmed by the 'other mind', I expect that you know that trying to engage the individual in a different mode of thinking about ordinary, day-to-day things, such as going to Tesco, having a bath, is like trying to haul them away from a safety blanket, or the source of life itself! To please you and not let on about the 'other mind', the individual may half-heartedly and absentmindedly go along with you and duck out at the first possible moment. This is often a problem in rehabilitation work.

Getting stuck in this way of thinking is only part of the story. To complete the exercise in which we try to put ourselves into the shoes of the person who is overwhelmed by the psychotic process and who has a psychotic illness we need to ask what other ingredients might make the experience what it is.

*Point 1*. We can imagine a state where we are entrapped in a dreamlike state in a recurring thought process. The feeling is that this thought process will not let go of us. It prevents us concentrating on day-to-day things like making a shopping list, having a bath, organising life. One person described this as like being asleep but awake at the same time, a very unpleasant experience. In the dream-like state an individual might be Alexander the Great or Jesus Christ or Buddha surrounded by visions of light, voices and noises of battles or whatever and the next moment be an awake but confused individual, being bombarded by the preoccupations of the delusional beliefs, a person who has to escape from the bombardment of the 'other mind' and get a meal together and get out of bed. The other mind wants the healthy self exclusively to itself and does its best to prevent the healthy self from looking outward into the world and to others. It is like a very large ferocious baby holding its mother's face in giant imprisoning hands and demanding total attention from the healthy self, resorting to vicious means to get its own way if necessary.

*Point 2.* So add to that hallucinations – these are probably produced by structural or biochemical brain abnormalities and may or may not be part of a psychotic illness. However the psychotic process uses them to distance the healthy person further from reality.

*Point 3.* Add to these what must be a result of 1 and 2, a turning inward, an isolation, a fear of reality, a fear of social interaction, a feeling that no one is on your side and no one can understand and you can't either. Being pulled into this dream-like vortex leads to an inability to move forward and a fear that life is passing you by. *Dread, futility, hopelessness, despair* set in. There is a sense of pointlessness and a fear that real life is never going to start. This is an extremely painful and distressing state.

*Point 4.* All this takes energy. So add to the above tiredness out of all proportion to any exertion that has taken place, loss of energy, an inability to initiate anything and a profound wish to escape and get under the duvet and stay there all day. Every minute of life feels like a burden.

*Point 5.* Add the fact that you may have done things which are seriously damaging, dangerous, embarrassing; and be appalled, embarrassed and uncomprehending, when functioning in the healthy self, by what you have done.

*Point 6.* Add medication, which makes you feel like a mental and physical zombie. It may make you perform peculiar movements of limbs and mouth, it may make you fatter than you ever have been in your life and unable to dredge up the motivation to find the right clothes. The voices may be dulled by the medication but so are you.

*Point 7.* Add to this the terror of being forcibly hospitalised in a strange lonely place with odd people the like of whom you have never seen before.

Well, if you have managed to get through this you can see that it adds up to a horrifying experience.

*2. How do we understand the fact that an individual attempting to cut his throat may on the one hand say 'I am Hitler and people are coming to punish me for my crimes – I have to kill myself'? And on the other hand that individual may be inquiring ten minutes later when his next therapy session is and worrying about perfectly ordinary things, such as whether he has enough money for the laundrette. This is called working in two minds. What is this idea of two minds about?*

Patients have been saying for years things like: 'I am like two people, Jekyll and Hyde. One minute I am like this and the next like a monster. I don't know what happened, it was not me.' Psychoanalytical and psychiatric workers have told them that this cannot be so.

But the patients were right – of course! A psychoanalyst called Wilfred Bion (1967) wrote about the presence of a psychotic and non-psychotic process in all of us. Dr Michael Sinason and Jocelyn Richards have taken the idea of working in 'two minds' further (Sinason, 1993, 1999; Richards, 1993, 2001). In the unit in which I work, the concept of 'two minds' informs all the therapy that we do and we find understanding it is helpful to sufferer, carer and therapist. Working in two minds means that rather than seeing an individual as one person, functioning from one mind in one body, it is as if two people were functioning from one body. That is to say, there is a healthy self and a psychotic self, which I refer to as the 'other mind', and both operate autonomously.

I shall talk about the early development of the 'other mind' later, since it develops in earliest infancy. First let us state baldly that the function of the 'other mind' is to keep the healthy self away from making meaningful contact with any person, thing or any fantasy of a relationship. This contact includes needing someone, getting meaningfully angry with someone, as well as making positive contact of any sort with the person or thing. The minute an awareness of wanting to make contact arises, a sense of shame at having such a need is triggered. The shame is either consciously felt or repressed and therefore not felt consciously. In either case the 'other mind' immediately takes over and all the delusional material takes over.

Why does the other mind do this? Because it believes that relationships are dangerous and lead to pain and suffering so they are to be avoided at all costs. It is doing its best to save the individual from the pain of intolerable feelings of falling to bits, disintegrating.

There has always been a tendency to blame family members as family interactions often precipitate psychotic behaviour. It may be the case that family relationships are healthy and creative. They may be destructive and harmful. Either way, mums and dads and siblings and other family members are usually the people we relate to most intensively in the first 15 years of life and so they are most likely to stimulate a sense of love, neediness or frustration. So of course, they would be prime movers in stimulating the 'other mind' and therefore being the target of the other mind and being regularly attacked and repulsed. However the other mind may not be acting toward the individual family member who is present at a particular moment. It may be reacting to a repressed, or forgotten experience of a much earlier frustration that is not consciously remembered but which is triggered by a particular interaction.

In other words, the sight of mum at a time when loneliness is experienced might bring back a very old and not even conscious memory of missing mum in infancy when she was away, perhaps ill in hospital and that can call out the 'other mind' and tip an individual into behaving in a way that is out of touch with reality.

A patient brought a long sharp knife concealed in clothing into the consulting room intending to kill me. Initially I did not know about the knife but, when the patient came in, it was possible to sense that the 'other mind' was present rather than the healthy person. I connected the negativity and destructiveness in the room with the fact that the patient might have been disappointed and angry that I had not able to be at the last session. I knew that this would have caused a feeling of neediness (conscious or unconscious), followed by a takeover by the other mind. So I said several times and in several ways that I did not blame the individual for being fed up. I said I thought the 'other mind' had taken over and was in the room. This was denied at first and later confirmed. Eventually there was a change in the atmosphere in the room, an easing up of tension, the knife was given up and when I eventually said: 'I wonder who wanted to kill me, you or the other mind?' The sad reply from the healthy self was: 'The other mind. *I* don't want to kill you.'

It is important to refer to the healthy self as *you* and to talk *about* the 'other mind', if possible giving it a name, which is neutral, not derogatory, a name chosen by the patient if possible. It takes time to learn how to address the two minds and how to make sense of why they turn up when they do. It is very important to avoid criticising or using negative names for the 'other mind'. It is worth bearing in mind that it does not like being talked about and will lash back viciously when the therapist, or family member talks about it with a patient's healthy self. This lash-back phenomenon is why people with psychosis in therapy get worse after some months of working with the 'other mind'. They may even require admission to hospital. This may not be a bad thing. The therapy sessions should continue during the admission. Gradually, over time, the healthy self becomes stronger and for some reason this slowly erodes the power of the other mind, which becomes much easier to manage.

It does take time but the results can be very gratifying. The principles outlined above can be used by family members and staff and should be understood and verbalised by staff doing family work.

*3. How do we understand in developmental terms the situation where an individual is entrapped in the 'other mind' – the psychotic process?*

The dreaded subject of 'blame' comes up whenever the genesis of psychosis from a psychological point of view is discussed.

Firstly, it would seem as if the template for the psychosis which develops later is laid down in early infancy. The person who spends most time with a very young infant is almost always the mother. The crucial early relationship between infant and mother is full of potential crises. There is no such thing as a perfect mother or a perfect infant. As Donald Winnicott (1976) said, the best one can hope for is a 'good enough' mother. All sorts of unavoidable accidents can happen which are out of human control. The infant might have mechanical difficulties feeding; the infant's mother might develop a breast abscess, or a serious illness and be unable to feed the infant as she might have wished. There might be a war on and bombing and terror might interrupt an otherwise healthy relationship.

Mothering is one of the hardest jobs on earth. It is the equivalent of being on call as a medical doctor every day and night for ten years or more. The mother can't even go to the lavatory in peace if her toddler is heading for the top of the stairs. If a mother has a migraine and is alone with her baby, her suffering must be unimaginable. And if a mother has a depressive or other mental illness and can't access her normal feelings, such as those of love, and wants to hide under a duvet and never get up, her suffering is similarly unimaginable. I find it incredible that some professionals have been so quick to lay blame at the door of mothers, who may have done their very best under impossible circumstances and who should in no way be landed with guilt on top of trying to cope with their child's psychosis. The *genesis* of the psychosis *may* be *related to events* in infancy which include a mother but the events are part of a much wider scenario. The whole idea of blaming and shaming is destructive and unhelpful. Therapy should be about *understanding.*

The first few months of life are a crucially sensitive time for all of us. The infant is extremely sensitive to the empathy and timing of his mother's eye gaze and his mother's voice in response to his own gaze and vocalisations.

Beebe and Lachman (2002, p. 93) have videoed the mother–infant interactions and have studied stills each taken at 1/12th of a second, looking at facial expression, gaze and head orientation in both mother and baby. They were looking at the engagement level between mother and infant amongst other things. In the interactions, factors such as time, space, affect (feeling) and arousal (level of excitability) were important. If these are properly matched, then it is possible to calm or stimulate an overexcited or an apathetic baby, to appropriately match the facial expressions as they change, to time these changes in a facilitating way and to produce vocal rhythms which match the babies' and so on. Perfect matching is impossible but repair of mismatches takes place. However if there is continual misregulation and mismatching, then this is laid down as a template in the infant's mind and there is forever an expectation of being 'misread', so to speak, which affects the individual's life in serious ways thereafter, not least because an infant attributes such failures to himself and feels *he* is useless if he is misunderstood.

If the infant has multiple carers or his mother is ill and unable to provide the matching in the first months or years, or his mother is being harassed or beaten and thus distracted by his father, then it is more likely that there will be difficulties later. I believe that this type of scenario increases the tendency to experience shame which is important in the genesis of the psychotic process, 'other mind'. I shall discuss this in question 5.

Genetic factors are important. Professor David Horrobin (Horrobin, 2001) in his excellent book, 'The Madness of Adam and Eve', has described the situation in which there are families where schizotypy (where an individual tends to be a loner, a bit paranoid, not sociable) is common and in these families there is often an over-representation of psychoses, psychopathy, alcoholism, artistic talent and brilliance in various fields. Schizoid people typically are loners who have difficulty with close relationships. The occurrence of these states may be connected to the fact that there is a deficiency of EPA (eicosapentaenoic acid, an omega-3 fatty acid), in certain families and this would interfere with crucial communications between various brain areas and predispose to mental illness. The deficiency may be due to the fact that there is not enough of it taken in by the body or that there is a difficulty in making it within the body, or that there was not enough available to pass from mother to foetus before birth.

Nearly every patient who has a psychotic illness that I see, has a history of one or several of the following: ADHD, dyspraxia (clumsiness), dyslexia (difficulty with reading and writing), dyscalculia (difficulty with figures), autism, Asberger's syndrome, oppositional disorder. There is growing evidence that these are connected with EPA deficiency. Nearly all the patients I see have what are called 'soft' neurological signs, that is, minor neurological abnormalities that are connected with severe psychoses (Manschreck, 2003).

So there is a complex interaction of neurobiological, chemical and psychological events that may lead to the initial laying down of a rather overlarge and overactive 'other mind' in infancy. This may be followed by the child developing difficulties which are first dealt with by the family who adjust themselves to accommodate the difficulties. The difficulties may take the form of restlessness at school, inability to pay attention, clumsiness. They may be put down to naughtiness and ignored by school teachers who are unaware of their significance and, in any case, do not have easy access to people who could offer diagnostic and management help.

It is when there is the threat of leaving home, and the possibility of having relationships with the opposite sex and being put into an environment where people will not adjust to an individual's peculiarities, that the first breakdown often occurs.

## 4. Where does EPA come into the equation?

It is interesting to note the enthusiasm generated by the TV series about Jamie Oliver's attempts to introduce nutritious fresh food into schools. Where children had been 'converted' from junk food to his freshly cooked dinners, with organic ingredients where possible, teachers reported that the children were less restless, concentrated better, did better in class at lessons and used asthma pumps less. This was within a few weeks of the change. This was not a formal high-level research project but it seemed to me to convey a very important message. It is obvious that what we eat must become part of the body and this in turn must affect health, behaviour, the way we feel and the efficiency with which the body works. It also affects the brain, which is made up mainly of fat and which needs omega-3 and omega-6 fats in addition to minerals and vitamins in order to function properly.

Similar positive effects were found in a pilot study in which prisoners were given nutritional supplements including EFAs (Horrobin, 2001, p. 225). The result was a 50% reduction in the levels of violence amongst the prisoners. In both cases above the government or Home Office did not react with what one might deem appropriate alacrity and enthusiasm – there was no funding granted for a larger trial in prisons by the Home Office and so far the relatively small amount of extra money for better school dinners is only available through reallocation of funds (I think this is still the case in 2010).

Professor Malcolm Peet, in a paper looking at dietary habits in different populations in the world, looks at correlations between the outcome of schizophrenia and dietary fat intake. A dietary intake of saturated fat (animal products) has an adverse effect, and the intake of polyunsaturated fats (especially those derived from fish) has a positive effect on the outcome of schizophrenia (Peet, 2003).

On the subject of mood disorders, Tanskanen et al. (2001) looked at a population of 3,204 individuals and concluded that ... the likelihood of having depressive symptoms was significantly higher among infrequent fish consumers than among frequent consumers.'

David Horrobin (2001) postulates that, from an evolutionary point of view, dietary change, most notably the eating of essential fatty acids (EFAs) – particularly the omega-3 fatty acids eicosapentaenoic acid (EPA) and docosahexaenoic acid (DHA) as well as the omega-6 fatty acid, arachidonic acid (AA) – was responsible for homo sapiens developing a larger and more efficient and creative brain. The experiment that succeeded in creating super-intelligent mice, the Dougie and Mensa mice, worked by the interactions of protein and phospholipids resulting in a marked increase of connections (dendrites) between the nerve cells in the brain. This would give weight to Horrobin's hypothesis about the importance of EFAs.

Both omega-3 and omega-6 fatty acids are vital to life, and they are not made by the body. They have to be taken in the diet. The omega-3 fatty acids are converted by the body to EPA and DHA. The omega-6 fatty acids are converted to AA (arachidonic acid) and DGLA (dihomogammalinolenic acid).

Normally neurotransmitters activate a substance called phospholipase A2 (PLA2) which causes a release of arachidonic acid (AA), an EFA as well as other fatty acids. AA is responsible for the inflammation and pain, which alert the individual that there is a problem and thus it has a protective function, protecting damaged areas of the body. For example it will stop the individual from moving and further damaging an infected joint. Then the PLA2 has to be turned off, so to speak, with the help of an enzyme called fatty acid coenzyme A ligase (FACL). If this does not happen the AA will leak away!

The *sudden* release of AA and its conversion to prostaglandins is necessary for the brain to work properly. It enables brain cells to communicate properly with each other, the skin to respond normally to stimulation, the stomach and intestines to contract properly and the membranes which keep body compartments from communicating with each other to fulfil their separate functions.

Both these mechanisms may go wrong. The niacin flush test is a test where niacin (Vitamin $B_3$) is either ingested or placed on the skin of a normal individual. This should result in flushing as the normal individual will produce AA and prostaglandins which cause flushing, provided the individual is not taking steroids or NSAIDs. It has been shown repeatedly that this reaction is absent in individuals with schizophrenia, because of the failure of one of these chemical steps. This reaction was used as a test in some early detection units to see if patients might be developing a psychotic illness. It might be useful to have it routinely available and used appropriately.

This abnormality in the niacin flush test may explain why patients with schizophrenia usually don't get rheumatoid arthritis (where there is adequate AA and a significant amount of pain and inflammation). Patients with schizophrenia often have a high pain threshold because of low levels of AA and they lose their psychotic symptoms when they have a high fever since fever is a powerful stimulus to the release of AA.

In patients with schizophrenia who have low levels of AA, the cells can be shown to have too much PLA2. It is thought that this excess of PLA2 results (as above) in a leaking out and loss of AA and other fatty acids so that the triggers (from a sudden high level of AA) for the normal and healthy chemical steps described above can't take place. High levels of activity of PLA2 (causing a leakage of AA) can be reduced by EPA. So EPA helps to conserve AA which is incorporated back into phospholipids with the help of the enzymes FACL and ACLAT.

Broadly speaking EPA is responsible for healthy brain function and DHA for healthy structural development. So eating a diet high in fatty fish and/or taking EPA and DHA (in the omega-3 fatty acids in fish oil) with the correct vitamins and minerals which act as coenzymes or cofactors, can help to re-establish, or establish more normal essential fatty acid (EFA) behaviour in the brain. EFAs are essential for the development and growth of the brain *in utero* and in infancy. These fatty acids are essential for the whole process of laying down memories, the proliferation of dendrites which results in richer connections, communication between cells and therefore different areas of the brain.

In fact, they are active in every single brain activity – as well as the functions of other organs like the skin and gut, the inner layer (endothelium) of blood vessels. The nerve bundle which fans out over the heart muscle, provides the nervous (electrical) stimulus for the heart to beat. This also functions more efficiently with healthy EFAs and the latter are being used to treat vascular diseases and are thought to prevent sudden death from disturbances in the heart rhythm. There is a strong association between depression and possibly manic-depressive disorders with cardiovascular disorders (such as heart attacks and strokes) (Horrobin, 2002).

Childhood disorders such as ADHD, dyslexia, dyspraxia, dyscalculia, autism, Asberger's, oppositional disorder, are associated with similar fatty acid abnormalities and, as I have said, when one takes a very careful history from patients and their parents, one frequently finds a history of one or more of the following: exaggerated clumsiness in childhood (possible dyspraxia), difficulty in paying attention at school, restlessness and overactivity, difficulties in making friends and so on. There is also often a history of dry skin, gastrointestinal problems, allergies (leading to asthma, eczema, hayfever) as these are also associated with lack of omega-3 fatty acids. The behaviours are all too often put down to naughtiness or just 'being difficult' or 'a bit quiet'. Dr Alex Richardson's website www.fabresearch.org has a wealth of information about these subjects.

The human brain has different functions on the right and left sides – lateralisation – although these differences are not absolute. Professor Tim Crowe has written that schizophrenia may be the result of something going wrong in the right / left communication of the brain.

Broadly speaking, the left brain is responsible for production and comprehension of speech – and also for verbally mediated affective (immediate feeling) and mood states and for less primitive states such as guilt and anxiety.

The right brain is responsible for visuospatial recognition, recognition of facial emotion. The right frontocortical brain is dominant for non-verbal mood, (often gloomy depressing types of things) as well as shame, disgust and elation.

Each side communicates through a structure called the corpus callosum which is a band of brain tissue which functions as a sort of switchboard allowing messages to constantly pass from right to left brain. There is also traffic from front to back and to deeper structures like the limbic system, responsible for feelings, and the autonomic nervous system, responsible for emotions of fight and flight. We need the communication between *all* parts of the brain to be possible and this requires adequate connections which function properly – and this in turn requires essential fatty acids (EFAs).

The right brain matures earlier than the left, has longer nerve cells which are more far reaching, develops very quickly especially between eight and ten months and is heavily involved in the infant's gaze behaviour. A mother and baby gazing into each other's faces, responding in an attuned way is very important indeed for development. 'The earlier developing right hemisphere is, more so than the later maturing left, deeply connected into the autonomic (fight and flight emotions), limbic (feelings) and arousal systems.' The right brain is dominant for the reception, expression and communication of emotion and for the *regulation* of affect. That means that if there is overexcitement or the reverse, the healthy right brain brings things back to midline (Schore, 2002).

I mention this as I have quite frequently asked patients who are in the grip of the 'other mind' (possibly implying maladaptive right brain activity) to cover the left eye and look into a light with the right eye. Because the fibres from the optic nerve at the back of the right eye mostly (but not completely) cross to the left side, the left brain is stimulated – that is, the area for more mature activities, symbolisation, speech production and comprehension. Patients almost invariably report a reduction in their psychotic symptoms, a decrease of agitation and possibly dread. One person said that he lost his voices and when he tried it at home he felt lonely and bereft without them! (This was despite the fact that he had also complained that the voices made it difficult to get on with ordinary living as they were so distracting and compelling.)

When I have asked patients to cover the right eye thus stimulating the right brain, it has caused discomfort and agitation in most people.

So I think it is possible that the psychotic process is dominant when the right brain is dominant and the left brain is for some reason inhibited. It would also seem that the regulatory capacity of the right brain is disturbed.

In conclusion, you will have realised that there is a great deal that can be said about this. It is difficult to prove or to demonstrate conclusively that one area of the brain is exclusively responsible for any one particular type of reaction as the brain is enormously complex and constantly changing in response to both the internal and external environment. Consider that a large match head's worth of your brain contains about a billion neural connections. There are about 10 billion neurons in the cerebral cortex which is the mantle covering the higher brain – that does not include the supporting cells – and a million billion connections in the cortical sheath (Edelman, 1992, Ch 3). The impulses have to flow readily from one part of the brain to another and it would seem that there is strong evidence to suggest that EFAs are essential for that process.

What seems to me more important is that in my clinical experience of giving people with severe mental disorder omega-3 fatty acids, the results have been impressive. Some people respond better than others. In some there is quite a rapid response in terms of an increase in energy and a decrease in tension – I am not sure what else to call an uncomfortable uptightness that is not exactly anxiety. In others there is a gradual lessening of the psychotic symptoms and more important, less difficulty in managing the symptoms. People report that it is easier to emerge from the prison of the 'other mind'. I believe it makes it easier for people to use the psychotherapy we offer and which I regard as an essential part of treatment. People with mood disorders sometimes notice a marked improvement. Many people diagnosed with schizophrenia also suffer painfully low mood and the omega-3 fatty acids may be reversing that aspect of the condition as well as the psychotic symptoms. In a single case study using EPA alone in an individual who was not able to take antipsychotic medication, there was a relief of symptoms and a positive change in brain structure demonstrated on scan (Puri et al., 2000).

There are numerous reports of subtle brain abnormalities in schizophrenia and I think that the fact that the brain can change its structure in response to treatment is heartening. This structural change has been shown to occur with psychotherapy (Martin et al., 2001) as well as other treatments such as EPA as mentioned above.

## 5. What about the importance of shame?

Most people know what it is like to feel engulfed by shame. It is an extremely unpleasant experience. It occurs when someone does or says something to make one feel very small. It involves the autonomic nervous system and predominantly the right brain.

If I were to walk into a room full of joyous enthusiasm and energy (the sympathetic nervous system uppermost) ready to give what I thought would be an exposition and everyone in the room responded by looking the other way or not noticing me, I would feel overcome by shame. I would blush (since the parasympathetic nervous system would take over and the sympathetic constriction of blood vessels is lost) and lower my eyes, and want to disappear under the floorboards. I would feel as if the whole of me had been annihilated. My blood pressure would drop. I would be unable to think. That is shame!

Bullying is a form of shaming and humiliating. If you have ever been bullied you will realise how difficult it is to think, how helpless and out of control one feels.

In infants this is a very important process. If the infant is trying to joyously get something across to her carer, and the carer does not respond, looks disgusted or as if assaulted by a bad smell (dissmell), or contemptuous, then the infant is plunged from a state of sympathetic arousal, joyous energy, to a state of shame and painful distress, low arousal and lack of responsivity. The infant turns her head away, lowers her eyes and becomes under aroused and unresponsive (parasympathetic state). This is not the healthy autoregulation whereby an over aroused infant can be helped by her carer (mother) with autoregulation into a more tranquil state but a propulsion into an intensified low arousal state which the infant cannot yet autoregulate.

The problem is that the infant then attributes blame to herself for any disasters in infancy and early childhood. So states of shame are felt to be due to the infant's inadequacy and 'badness'. That is more tolerable than feeling that the universe (carer, mother) is totally out of one's control. At least one can try to improve oneself – in theory!

That results in a negative view of the developing self and potential which makes her more prone to shame and a vicious circle is set up with excessive proneness to shame and attendant unresponsiveness and later difficulty in learning, with the gaps in knowledge accumulating, resulting in criticism for incompetence and more shaming. And so a pattern is set.

*'Use or lose'* brain cells is an interesting principle! There is a massive pruning (dying off) of redundant brain cells at around about the age of four years and again later in early teens. During early learning phases there are selective increases in areas of brain. For example, neuroimaging at Dr Paul Thompson's laboratory showed that the brain systems specialised for learning language grew extremely rapidly from the age of six until puberty with a dramatic shutting down of growth around ages 11–15 coinciding with the end of the well-known period during which children learn new languages.

Taxi drivers in London who have to learn 'the knowledge' to qualify for a black cab job have been found to have enlargement of the hippocampus which is involved in memorising.

Some studies have shown that some patients with schizophrenia have a smaller hippocampus than normal and other studies show that in people with schizophrenia, the usual brain tissue loss between 13 and 18 gained momentum and losses were substantially greater than in normal people.

A study of children with ADHD (attention deficit hyperactivity disorder) had a smaller brain volume and other features that were compatible with hypothesised dysfunction of the right-sided prefrontal-striatal systems. The right side of the brain associated with shame, disgust and so on is involved.

There are many studies showing similar findings. It makes one wonder about the 'use it or lose it' principle – and the reverse – use it and it grows!

If *shame* is a constant feature in early infancy and childhood, the areas of brain involved, the right brain, will be overused. Perhaps it is kept going instead of being pruned? Being constantly beset by states of shame makes learning anything *much* more difficult. Registration of information cannot take place. There is therefore less to remember and I wonder if the hippocampus is underused. This may account for there being a relatively small hippocampus in some people with ongoing psychoses. It may also account for loss of brain cells in other areas since shame results in a shutting down, turning away, 'brakes on' kind of attitude to life.

Whereas in childhood the family tends to work around and accommodate deficits in the individual who is at risk, the situation becomes more difficult in later life. The second pruning of brain cells occurs in adolescence. It is at school-leaving that children are faced with the prospect of leaving home, mixing with people who don't accommodate their deficits, having sexual relationships and being generally more social as well as needing to settle for a career and so on. The accumulated deficits then become a more noticeable problem and it is at that time that the first psychotic symptoms become manifest. They are often hidden and even dealt with by self-treatment with illicit drugs. A vicious circle is set up whereby school work is abandoned, social activities don't take place, the brain is underused and if there is anything in the 'use it or lose it' principle, unused brain cells will be pruned. This makes it more difficult to 'catch up' with what one has missed during those years.

Getting back to shame, it is possible, on close observation, to see that the 'other mind' takes over when shame kicks in. The shame is not always consciously felt, as it may be too painful to have in the forefront of the mind. It may therefore be experienced as irritation or anger or even rage associated with a sensation of being criticised or having unfair demands made. Or it may just manifest as a turning away from the therapist to be intrigued, pleased or frightened by hallucinations or to become preoccupied with delusional ideas about being a famous inventor or something of that nature.

It seems that it is very important therefore, to deal with shame in therapy alongside other treatments so that a process whereby the individual is freed up to learn – that is to register, take in, store and process new information – can take place. After all the brain can change, neuroplasticity is a fact. It does not take place quickly but it happens and people need to have the chance to get the brain registering, absorbing, processing and storing information again – a situation that is not possible where there is excessive proneness to shame.

Schore (2002) has written that early trauma in the form of a particular type of insecure attachment in the first two years of life has serious impact on the right brain which is dominant for attachment, and regulation of stress and feeling intensity. This results in proneness to PTSD. Again taking a careful history from patients makes one aware that the nature of the experience of the other mind and the content of the experience can sometimes look like a type of PTSD related to the early infantile trauma.

Why do I say that? The 'other mind' experiences are so vivid and real that they resemble the PTSD experiences in adults. For example, individuals with PTSD reliving a drowning disaster can smell the water, hear the screams, feel the bodily pain and experience the terror in flashbacks and nightmares.

Experience by the other mind can be similarly very vivid and ongoing. For example I spoke to a patient, Jeremy, who believed that he had deformed his nose by performing a certain action. He felt he was so ugly that he could not leave the house, could not let his adult children see him and had to leave work. He felt intense shame, a dysphoria, whenever he looked at his face. In reality his nose did not appear abnormal in any way. When I later spoke to his mother, she told me that she had had a depressive psychosis when he was born and had a delusional belief that her nose was bent and that she was too ugly for the baby to look at! So this mother had been turning her face from her baby Jeremy who in a primitive, infantile way might have felt *he* was too ugly for his mother to gaze upon with the same attendant shame and dysphoria!

Another example is of a young girl, Clarissa, who, every evening, when acutely ill, would, in a state of distress and hunger, make a large meal, eat a little of it and then give up and throw the food away. She would obsessively repeat the process again and again throughout the night. This went on for months. Speaking to her mother, I was told that she had had a mechanical problem that made eating (sucking) very difficult in the first three weeks of life. She would suck at the breast and try desperately hard to get some milk, get very little and then fall back exhausted. She would then cry pitifully as she was hungry and then another attempt was made . Eventually the mechanical problem was put right and normal feeding resumed but the trauma was too much to metabolise and the baby grew up to be psychologically fragile and eventually developed an established psychotic illness.

Yet another young woman, Jane, was quite seriously ill with a psychotic process that, amongst other delusional symptoms, manifested as a disorder of thinking. She could not speak and use words to make herself understood and she could not make sense of what was said *to* her. This was a distressing experience and often her verbal efforts were made in a very loud distressed voice. The thought disorder included paragrammatisms (incorrect grammar), neologisms (making up words), derailment, knight's move thinking (going off at a tangent) and so on, indicating that the left brain, responsible for production and comprehension of speech was not functioning at these times. What was interesting was that, when the healthy self was communicating, none of this was present. This young lady could both understand and speak clearly. The patient's mother told me that she had had a severe and extremely painful infection immediately after the birth of her baby and had had a severe depressive illness which made her unable to focus on her baby. So the early concentrated interactions between infant and mother as described above, which would have made sense of the baby's communication which in turn would have been communicated to the infant, were absent. What manifested in the other mind was the vivid, terrifying and painful experience of being not understood and not understanding. 'I don't understand' was a phrase Jane frequently used.

One of the most ill patients I ever met, who was rarely off an acute ward and rarely off a section of the Mental Health Act, was similarly seriously and almost permanently thought disordered. His speech was almost incomprehensible and gave the impression that there must be significant brain damage. However, every now and then there was an island of near normality. During those times, this individual spoke clearly, understood what was being said, had a good vocabulary, an apparently normal intellect and wrote things down clearly! Two things come to mind as I write this, the first is the utter tragedy of the situation for that individual and his family. And the second is that this individual must have had a potentially intact left brain. However, the right brain seemed to have been dominant most of the time. I did not know about the extent of the significance in mental health of lateralisation then, as it was many years ago. In retrospect, this gives credibility to the idea that in chronic psychoses *one* of the difficulties is the proper communication between right and left brain.

There are many examples of this nature that have made me think that the psychotic process is a kind of PTSD that is ongoing, vivid and that reproduces in some way an early trauma.

The usual experience that most people have of repeating old events is called repetition compulsion. For example, you will know that some people repeatedly make the same mistakes in choosing a partner. This is very different from the gripping, urgent nature of PTSD, which is a form of repeating in experiential terms a painful event. It also differs from the imprisoning and all consuming nature of a takeover by the 'other mind', the psychotic process which makes it impossible to function from the healthy self. The repeated actions of Jeremy, Clarissa and Jane are only three of many examples of what seem to be repeated enactments of an early painful situation, usually occurring at a time before the infant can talk.

PTSD is notoriously difficult to treat, and so is psychosis, which is why it is essential to make every effort to understand these conditions from every possible angle.

## 6. What can we do about this?

If you were attempting to train an individual to run the marathon, you would know that there are all sorts of angles to consider. The muscles need to be built up so several varieties of regular training, (running, gym exercises, etc.) would be necessary. To build up muscle tissue, the right sort of food has to be eaten and damaging substances (animal fat, drugs and alcohol and cigarettes, etc.) would have to be avoided. Healthy sleeping habits would be encouraged as well as the right attitude so that a positive psychological state would spur the individual on through training and the final race.

You would know that running practice alone, in the absence of an adequate diet, would be a waste of time. Similarly if the individual ate the most propitious diet without running training, the prospects of completing the marathon would be poor. And if the individual was too demoralised to run they would probably drop out or not try hard. And so on.

Surely the same principles apply to treating a chronic psychotic illness!

## PHARMACOTHERAPY

Let us deal with pharmacotherapy first. Most patients will be on some sort of antipsychotic medication. This is of course helpful as it reduces the vividness of the hallucinations and delusions. Analysis of the FDA database has shown that average symptom reduction was 16.6% with newer antipsychotics and 17.3% with traditional neuroleptics (Khan et al., 2001). The newer antipsychotics have fewer side effects and that is a great advantage but they are not free of side effects. It is important for each individual to be on what suits him best in terms of having the fewest side effects and preventing hallucinations and delusions from intruding into daily life as much as possible. What suits one individual may not suit another. The newer antipsychotics, particularly clozapine, work better with omega-3 fatty acids (see below). It is thought that the older antipsychotic medications inhibit the action of omega-3 fatty acids.

On this point, it is interesting that, according to the WHO, in Third World countries fewer patients go on to develop severe defect states in chronic schizophrenia, with negative symptoms, than in the developed world. It has been postulated by some that this may be because people in the Third World take less antipsychotic medication because it is simply not available. It costs too much. Since lack of EPA (a fraction of omega-3 fatty acids) is a problem from the outset in schizophrenia, if individuals are given the older types of antipsychotic medications regularly, then whatever EPA is present will be inhibited by certain antipsychotic medications and the likelihood of more severe chronic symptoms would be greater.

On balance, it seems important that the lowest, most effective dose of medication be taken, as it helps the individual who is overwhelmed by psychotic symptoms to function better. It also helps patients make use of psychotherapy, which can be difficult if the psychotic symptoms are overwhelming the healthy self.

I shall not be going into the pros and cons of the different types of medication as there are many publications available on the subject and it is not the remit of this chapter. In addition, new findings emerge about these medications every few months!

## FOOD

In order for the brain to use the psychotherapy, family work and so on and, for that matter, to respond to medication, it needs to have the *right food*.

In a long-term follow-up of a single patient with schizophrenia treated with ethyl-EPA alone, there was not only a sustained remission of schizophrenic symptoms, but MRI scanning showed 'changes in ventricular volume, VBR, white matter and cerebral cortex consistent with a reversal of ventricular atrophy' (Puri & Richardson, 2003, p. 387) (Puri et al., 2000).

If neuroplasticity (change in the brain tissue, shape) is a fact and if we want the right areas of the brain to develop, we must feed it the substances that help that process along. Omega-3 fatty acids derived from fish oil contain EPA and DHA, the DHA being responsible for structure and the EPA for function.

Cod liver oil is not recommended. This is because the Vitamin A contained in many cod liver oil products is excessive. This can reduce the effectiveness of Vitamin D which is SO important in bone health, immunity, mood control and many other body functions. I am aware that there are many brands of cod liver oil containing different amounts of Vitamin A and D, and that in the developing countries Vitamin A deficiency can be a problem so this may not apply there.

For *vegetarians*, the only alternative at the moment is flax seed oil which contains the omega-3 fatty acid, alpha linolenic acid. It takes several steps for this to be converted by the body into EPA and the enzymes necessary for these steps can be blocked by various factors such as virus infections. So it is not the best source of EPA or DHA. I understand that some companies are trying to manufacture EPA from non-fish sources. (A relatively new development is the oil derived from krill which has EPA and DHA in it. In addition there is a company, V-Pure, that makes DHA from algae. However it contains a relatively small amount of EPA.)

It is important to take a good quality omega-3 oil and not the cheapest supermarket brand that one can find. I had patients who had run out of the recommended oil and as a temporary measure, had bought and taken a cheap supermarket brand and had as a result relapsed. This was put right when the original fatty acid was consumed. (As an aside I have to say here that where there is a big improvement to start with, and a deterioration on stopping the fatty acids, resuming the same does *not* always result in the same initial improvement. This peculiar situation can also be observed with conventional antidepressants. I do not know the reason for this.)

As far as a recommended dose is concerned, work so far indicates that for people with a chronic psychotic illness (schizophrenia), 2 gm a day of EPA as part of the omega-3 oil is optimal (Peet & Horrobin, 2002). DHA alone does not have the same positive effect (Horrobin, 2001, p. 217). There has been some evidence that 1 gm of EPA daily is optimal for mood disorders. More research needs to be done in this area.

There are those who say that EPA alone is sufficient as EPA is converted to DHA. However there is also doubt about the body's ability to reliably convert EPA to DHA. One case study was of an individual who had been taking omega-3 fatty acids for some years and an oil containing only EPA and no DHA for two years had blood levels of fatty acids done and was found to have NORMAL levels of EPA but LOW levels of arachidonic acid and LOW levels of DHA. (Of course these are serum levels and may not reflect levels in the brain, but that is the case for most of the available biochemical measures that we depend upon.)

The point is that DHA is responsible for developing brain STRUCTURE and is therefore particularly important in the developing infant's brain. I understand that the premature baby-milk formula contains added DHA for this reason. It is also particularly important in older people. The ageing brain needs DHA.

Thus women intending to conceive or who are pregnant ought to take a mixture of DHA and EPA together with EPO. Products containing extra DHA for infants and for pregnant women are available. Older people ought to take DHA-containing products.

There are those who are of the opinion that DHA, being a small molecule, degrades rapidly and produces free radicals and they advise against taking DHA. Free radicals are naturally produced all the time in the body and with a healthy diet and life style can be adequately dealt with. This can be helped by the addition of antioxidant supplements such as vitamin E. Vitamin E is included in some of the omega-3 oils.

The omega-3 fatty acid ought to be taken with a good quality multivitamin, and a multimineral ought to be taken separately at least an hour before all food as green leafy vegetables and grains bind the minerals to form phytates which are then not absorbed. The reason for taking these substances is NOT because of a vitamin or mineral deficiency, but because minerals and vitamins are coenzymes or cofactors necessary for the necessary chemical steps to take place.

Some patients on the above regime taking EPA and vitamins have improved and reached a plateau after some months. Discussion with a biochemist working with fatty acids has indicated that these patients may have run out of arachidonic acid (AA), an omega-6 fatty acid, which is available via oil of evening primrose, which contains gammalinolenic acid which is converted to AA. So in some people, it may be advisable to take up to 1–2 gm of oil of evening primrose. Having said that, the Western diet is usually top heavy in omega-6 fatty acids and that is *not* a desirable state of affairs. It is important to get the omega-3/omega-6 ratio correct and for that it would be desirable to have available blood testing. However none of the relevant blood tests are available on the NHS and are costly to have privately.

Unfortunately, the NHS is in the thrall of private drug companies (Pollock, 2004, Ch 1) whose job it is to sell chemicals that are not in the public domain, for vast sums of money. (I strongly recommend every health service user in this country to read Professor Allyson Pollock's book 'NHS plc' for a mind-blowing and enlightening experience.) Omega-3 fatty acids, which *are* in the public domain, which are relatively cheap and free of side effects, are not available from the NHS except in a few hospitals, and then under certain conditions. I understand that the Maudesley Hospital at the time this chapter was originally written in 2006, allowed prescription of omega-3 fatty acids for 'treatment resistant schizophrenia'. The term 'treatment resistant' surely means that if a 'cure' is not effected, with return to health and a state where medication is not required, then the patient is treatment resistant. This is so for most patients who are stuck with taking antipsychotic medication. So in reality, all patients who need ongoing treatment for psychoses should take omega-3 fatty acids.

Some people who would be expected to respond to omega-3 fatty acids fail to do so. Where it is possible to take blood levels of fatty acids, it can be demonstrated in some that the EPA, DHA and AA taken orally are *not absorbed*. This can be corrected by adjusting other aspects of the diet, to facilitate absorption of the fatty acids, after which blood levels increase and there is clinical improvement.

David Horrobin (2001, p. 190) discusses the impact of nutritional changes over the last 500–15,000 years. Horrobin states that F. C. Dohan drew attention to the adverse effects of some grains, which may change the metabolism of essential fatty acids and interfere with the acquisition of adequate EPA. Gwynneth Hemmings (1989) has advised avoidance of certain grains (particularly wheat) and has obtained excellent results in some individuals.

As I write this, I am aware of the appalling dilemma of some people with chronic psychoses, who also have frightful skin and lung allergies and who are sick of taking medication and attending clinics and having to listen to professionals. It is so hard to ask them to give up certain foodstuffs and take omega-3 fatty acids in addition to everything else that they have to endure, and yet it may be a life-changing move. One has to face the fact that sometimes the cure feels worse than the illness when seen from the bottom of the hill! We all need to think together, to work together to find a way of encouraging these people to try every possible option.

Omega-3 fatty acids can also be effective in mood disorders including depressive illness and bipolar disorders as well as in ADHD, dyspraxia, some cases of dyslexia, autism and Asberger's syndrome. Some of the symptoms of EPA deficiency apart from manifesting in the above ways are excessive thirst, frequent urination, dry skin, dry hair, brittle nails, dandruff, and follicular keratosis. I mentioned previously that Dr Alex Richardson's website www.fabresearch.org is full of information.

A recent randomised controlled trial (RCT) looking at the use of omega-3 fatty acids came to the following conclusion: 'Long-chain omega-3 PUFAs reduce the risk of progression to psychotic disorder and may offer a safe and efficacious strategy for indicated prevention in young people with subthreshold psychotic states' (Amminger et al., 2010). Prevention is the MOST important aspect of any discussion about mental, or any other illness. So this is a very important study.

I do find it incredible that omega-3 fatty acids are not available generally on the NHS, especially since to date there have been no serious side effects. It is a substance which, in the experience of many of those who have prescribed it, and those who have used it, has a positive effect on an indescribably unpleasant and crippling cluster of illnesses. In some cases it makes a substantially positive difference to an individual's life. In others it results in a subjective experience of less tension. It often achieves the latter quite quickly although theoretically it takes about six weeks to get into the brain cells. It makes it easier for individuals to manage the psychotic experiences and to use psychotherapy more effectively.

There have been anecdotal reports that very large doses of omega-3 fatty acids (the figure of 10 gm was quoted), taken by people who are withdrawing from drugs (I think this mainly referred to prescribed drugs such as antidepressants), can result in states of agitation or manic-like symptoms, but this was said to be uncommon. I have not been aware of anyone prescribing such large amounts.

One of the arguments against prescribing it that has been put to me is that the trials of omega-3 fatty acids do not involve large enough numbers of subjects. I would point out that large drug companies have the money to finance very large trials whereas the smaller companies producing EPA simply don't have the money. In addition there is an argument against the trials with very large numbers of subjects. The statistics in very large drug trials, because of the large numbers, can show a significant positive treatment effect that is qualitatively very small indeed. The reverse is true of smaller trials where there has to be a relatively large positive qualitative treatment effect to make the statistics significant.

Thus, I ask nearly all the patients who are referred to my department for psychotherapy to take omega-3 fatty acids as it helps the psychotherapy to have an effect. Unfortunately we do not at this time have facilities for measuring blood levels of fatty acids or PLA2. I strongly recommend reading David Horrobin's 'The Madness of Adam and Eve' (2001) which is a good read and a mine of information on evolution, schizophrenia, genetics and essential fatty acids.

## PSYCHOTHERAPY

If regular running is the training for the marathon, then psychotherapy is its equivalent in terms of training for travelling through life.

In my department we use psychoanalytically informed psychotherapy. This is not classical psychoanalysis and it uses cognitive elements. For people with chronic psychoses, therapy is offered for a year or more as it seems obvious that an illness that has taken so many years to develop is not going to be reversed in a few months. This *is* cost effective as in the long run it cuts down on the number of revolving door admissions, crises involving suicide or homicide attempts and so on.

Cognitive behavioural therapy is offered by other departments for shorter periods and can be quite helpful with less severely ill people and those who find it too painful to ask *why*? As well as *what*? However the effect often wears off and in my experience, patients are often re-referred for traditional psychotherapy or simply sent back to the psychiatric outpatient department or to the GP.

The problem that we have is to find supervisors trained in psychoanalytical psychotherapy, who can work with an understanding of the 'other mind' as there are few people who have both experience with severe illness (and who can therefore recognise risk), and who know how to work in this way.

The aim of psychotherapy is to build up and strengthen the healthy self and to lessen the negative, not to say paralysing, effect of the 'other mind', the psychotic process, on the individual's life. This lays a path for an individual to be able to discover what he wants to do with his life and to make a start at doing it. There are many processes which have to be worked at during the therapy. They can't all be discussed here.

However, at the start a major concern is to facilitate differentiation between the healthy self and the 'other mind'. Later, quite a lot later, comes the problem of how to negotiate loss – to start with, the loss of the life that could have been lived. No one can relive infancy, childhood or the last 15 or 30 years in optimal circumstances. It is agonising to suddenly realise what *might have been*. Younger people who have had no mental illness don't understand how unbearably painful this is. Older people, who suddenly find they lose the use of a limb or one of the senses, might have an inkling. When an individual who has been ill for 20 years suddenly starts saying in great distress: 'What have I done with my life?' the mourning process may have started. So negotiating loss is one of the tasks.

To achieve this the individual has to be able to 'take in' the therapy, which is impossible when shame is an overwhelming factor. A crucial aspect of psychotherapy is that it reduces shame, and thus enables registration, processing and storing of new information. This facilitates the experiencing, taking in, of a good experience which can to some extent make up for or counterbalance the early traumatic experiences. It strengthens the healthy self and allows the individual to understand and manage the 'other mind'.

There are various types of psychoanalytically informed psychotherapy starting with group and individual therapy. Group psychotherapy is very helpful in allowing individuals who have difficulty in relating to others to find a way of doing so and feeling accepted. I call this horizontal work as opposed to the vertical work of individual therapy! It is very useful to understand the operation of the 'other mind' in a group and it makes it possible to discuss how it operates and reduces shame.

Individual psychotherapy, from the outset, promotes as much understanding about the 'other mind' as is possible. The division between healthy self and the 'other mind' needs to be clarified. The factors that prompt the 'other mind' to take over need to be discovered so that pre-emptive action can be taken. A way of avoiding fighting against the 'other mind' and developing an understanding and tolerance of it is important and saves a lot of energy. All this leads to developing a way of talking *about* the 'other mind'. This is anathema to the 'other mind', which lashes back, so to speak. But this process is very helpful to the healthy self and facilitates the growth of an observing self (metacognition) which is part of that healthy self. This enables an individual to ask herself: 'Why am I feeling like this at this moment?' or 'Is this me or is it the "other mind"?' It is also very helpful to carers who are often subjected to attacks by the other mind, causing distress to the carer and the sufferer.

I was talking to a young man who had a severe illness, John, in an assessment in a perfectly ordinary way about real day-to-day concerns. I had been talking to him about the 'other mind' and he was beginning to distinguish between what was his healthy self and what came from the 'other mind'. He was able to concentrate and to express something of his current difficulties. His mother then came in, sat down and said nothing. With no warning John turned to her and said in an excessively loud complaining voice: 'You can't expect me to say much more than this. Why do you always want me to be different? How am I supposed to cope with all that? It is not fair.'

His mother was embarrassed, tried to smile and brush it off. She said: 'It is alright John, I haven't said anything. I don't expect anything of you.'

I said to him: 'John, a moment ago you were talking to me about your daily problems and you were feeling quite comfortable talking. What has happened?'

John: 'I don't know.'

DCL: 'I think the "other mind" is telling you that your mother is criticising you even though she has said nothing.'

For a moment he was about to argue and then his face changed. He smiled with some relief and said: 'Yes that's right. *I* don't think she is criticising me.'

We went on to discuss what had happened in more detail. I suspected that the presence of his mother had stimulated in him a need for her to be a support to him or to be containing. The awareness of need almost always occasions a sense of uncomfortable shame in those who are vulnerable to shame. The feeling is often not consciously felt by the individual but can be felt by those around. I call it pass-the-parcel shame. His mother felt it and I felt it too, as his response was inappropriate. What people do when shame is bypassed is to get angry and sometimes ragingly angry, even murderously angry. Both the need for and anger with his mother constitute making contact with her. This is the trigger for the 'other mind' to appear. It will say, either as a 'loud thought' or an hallucinatory voice: 'See she is looking at you in THAT way and she is thinking you are no good – you tell her off; have a good shout at her and get rid of her. You don't need her in your life ...' and so on and so forth.

This effectively offends the other person, in this case John's mother, and cuts all meaningful contact, which is just what the 'other mind' wants.

It was a relief to John and to his mother to understand that the other mind operates autonomously and does not reflect what John's healthy personality is feeling or wants.

When more of the healthy self is available, it is accessible to conventional psychotherapy and can be strengthened and given agency as a result.

Both *art* and *music therapy* can use an understanding of the other mind in group and individual settings. For individuals who have a disorder of thinking and who have great difficulty making themselves understood, and in understanding what is being said to them, music and art therapy used in this way can be a lifeline and can lead to the ability to use language. In the department I was heading art therapy was outstandingly helpful for some people and a colleague of mine who did our MSc in the psychodynamics of psychoses was using music therapy with an understanding of the other mind, with patients with whom no one else could deal. 'Both music and language can prime the meaning of a word, and music can, as language, determine physiological indices of semantic processing' (Koelsch et al., 2004). In other words it may be a way of getting through initially to patients who are inaccessible to ordinary conversation. How valuable that would be! How important for patients who cannot communicate but need to desperately!

## PSYCHOEDUCATION

Psychoeducation is a very important part of the treatment of any chronic illness. It is so important to explain to patients and carers something about psychoses and the management and treatment of the conditions. This would include recognition of early signs of first illness, explaining the origins and workings of the 'other mind' and how to handle it, how the brain works and changes, how to recognise the first indicators of recurrence of psychosis and what to do about it as well as strategies for the carers and the patient to help cope with the vicissitudes of an ongoing illness. Psychoeducation multi-family groups have been run and researched by Professor William McFarlane who has demonstrated very good results (McFarlane et al. 2000; McFarlane, 2001).

I found that the little psychoeducation I was able to offer – little because of time and staff limitations – had far-reaching effects. I explained to patients as clearly as I could about the nature, possible origins and ways of management as I have outlined in the article. This was done at the assessment interview and handouts were supplied and other sources of information were given. There were instances where it was realised that the children of the patients being assessed had one of the problems mentioned above; they were given fatty acids and even psychotherapy and the whole family constellation changed for the better.

## FAMILY WORK

Family work, with families of ill individuals, with an understanding of the 'other mind' principle is extremely important. Understanding the 'other mind' is a very effective way of decreasing 'high expressed emotion' (high EE) which can exacerbate the sufferer's symptoms. Put simply, people in families wind each other up and it does *none* of the family members any good. It can precipitate relapse and a worsening of the clinical condition in people with psychoses. It is a huge relief to a concerned family member to be able to differentiate between the patient's healthy self and an autonomously operating 'other mind' which simply wants to offend anyone who gets close to the sufferer. They feel much more able to step back from what can be offensive or hurtful attacks from the 'other mind' and to wait for the healthy self to become accessible. They are also more able to see their own contributions to bringing out the 'other mind' and to learn to avoid them.

## CARERS' TRAINING GROUPS

Carers' training groups seem to me an enormously important

weapon in the treatment armoury. There are thousands of carers all over the UK who are in the grip of chronic frustration about shortfall in services and the frustration about the chronicity of the illnesses. They are often overwhelmed by the heartbreak of seeing an individual they love unable to live a creative life, and driven up the wall by the unhelpful or uninformative responses by one or all members of the psychiatric team looking after the patient. They are given conflicting information and instructions and are often in a state of ongoing stress. This is not healthy for them and has a knock-on effect on the patient and rest of the family.

It would be desirable in all Trusts to set up training for carers who can run groups for other carers. The groups would be a mixture of psychoeducation and support and would include information about all the subjects that have been discussed above. Carers' groups differ little from the psychoeducation groups, but they could become a formal training arena. They would also include *any* person the patient regarded as carer, or upon whom the patient depended in some way. So it would not only include family but neighbours, friends or any involved individual.

Perhaps carers would be able to run social events. Patients who are chronically ill tend to avoid socialising. Simple things like having tea or a meal with others in a social setting may become an ordeal. There is a need to offer the opportunity for development of social skills in an accepting environment. This would increase the confidence of those who are gradually benefiting from the above regime and facilitate some kind of socialisation process.

## LIFESTYLE

Attention to general lifestyle would become part of the socialisation process. Patients with chronic psychoses tend to eat irregularly with a preponderance of junk food, take little exercise, and retire very late and wake at midday! I have already said that it is postulated that the communication and correlation between right and left brain may be defective. The fact that neurological soft signs (NSS) which show up on neurological testing (Manschreck, 2003) and are common in schizophrenia may be related to this. To facilitate change for the better, which may involve structural brain changes which require facilitating chemicals such as EPA, DHA and other nutrients and brain exercises the following need to receive attention:

a. Healthy eating is important in any rehabilitation programme and I refer back to Jamie Oliver's discoveries in the schools.

b. Some kind of regular activity such as voluntary work, sheltered work or attendance at MIND helps to develop some kind of routine in sleeping and waking.

c. Physical exercise including brain exercises might improve right – left brain activity. I am told that Tai Chi is designed to do exactly that! I have been greatly impressed by what I have seen of it.

The *New Scientist* carried an article on the benefits of brain exercises. The reference is given below. The author seemed impressed by the results of the brain training package provided by a certain company. In the assessments I did, I showed patients a few simple brain exercises and advocated ways of encouraging transcallosal (right to left) brain activity. Few patients did the exercises! Of course no *one* thing is right for any complex illness so the proposed miracle cure is highly unlikely. However brain exercises may be of use.

## CONCLUSION

When Professor Robin Murray was asked, I think in the early 2000s, on radio what he would do if he was told he was a schizophrenic, he said he would get another psychiatrist – or something like that. I think he was implying that what we call schizophrenia is not a discrete illness but along a continuum of illnesses and that schizophrenia has been given a bad press. I also like to give a quote attributed to a psychoanalyst, Bion (1967), who has been a major influence in thinking about psychoses and the practice of psychoanalytical psychotherapy. He said there is no such thing as a schizophrenic, only an individual suffering from schizophrenia – implying that there is always a healthy person underneath.

I think both these sentiments are important and accurate. I prefer to refer to an individual with a psychotic or chronic psychotic illness rather than a 'schizophrenic'.

Whatever the name, chronic psychotic illnesses are multifaceted in their genesis, presentation and recovery process. As I have stated, patients with these illnesses often have soft neurological signs, gut problems, skin problems, allergies, and a history of ADHD or dyspraxia (clumsiness), dyscalculia, dyslexia, autism or Asberger's syndrome. Therefore, logically the treatment has to be multifaceted.

Just giving antipsychotic medication at the infrequent outpatient visits and supplying a short CPN visit every two weeks and an injunction to attend MIND is inadequate. After all a diabetic with eye complications and leg ulceration has all three conditions treated in their own right.

Chronic psychoses can be devastating illnesses. A young person who has a good or average school history can slide into a psychotic illness and never get back to a normal achieving self. This may mean having to put up with a life-changing illness for the rest of his or her life. It may mean giving up all previous aspirations, giving up the idea of a career, a normal social life, truly independent living and periods of being free of prescribed drugs that cause side effects. It may mean being overweight, tired and 'zonked' all the time because the only drugs which control hallucinations are the ones with the side effects. It may mean having to face dread, futility, hopelessness and despair every day.

Less severe manic depressive psychoses can make it difficult to function normally and can sap the confidence, energy, and ability to live a normal life, making it difficult if not impossible to work and function adequately. Even if people get back to work they may have to deal with inner bleakness and phases of dread and futility and despair that are unbearably painful.

Chronic depression may not be as devastating as the above but the quality of life that sufferers face is not desirable to say the very least and at worst can lead to difficulties with functioning in everyday life.

Psychiatry is not a 'sexy' speciality. Chronic psychoses are not 'sexy' illnesses that attract large amounts of money and personnel interested in doing research – unlike cardiac disease, cancer or infertility. And prevention is not a 'sexy' business. But the fact remains that chronic psychoses (including schizophrenia) are amongst the most debilitating and painful illnesses that exist, and they carry high rates of suicide. Not only that but they have an effect on a wide circle of people around the sufferer, as well as on the Health Service in terms of cost and the country as a whole in terms of benefits paid and numbers unemployed. So if the lifetime prevalence of schizophrenia is 0.5% to 1.5%, an *awful* lot of people are adversely affected.

That more money is not spent on prevention, early detection, providing proper treatment and management of the illnesses seems to me to be a scandal. If a fraction of the money spent on useless wars were spent constructively in this way, many people's lives might be improved.

In a news website dated Thursday, 24th March 2005, 01:00 GMT, the following was written: 'One in six people are affected by mental health problems. Mental health patients should be given more choice about their treatment, a leading think-tank says. The Institute for Public Policy Research study said patients should not miss out on the wider NHS drive to offer options for treatment.

'Researchers called on the government to give patients their own budgets to spend on a range of therapies, medications and support when possible.'

And later: 'The paper, "A Good Choice for Mental Health", said that, when possible, patients should be offered a range of counselling, medication, psychological therapies and complementary medicine for their care package ... And they said GPs should not be the only access point to services.'

This may be a way forward. Perhaps better information about mental illness and the treatment options and the way mental health in the NHS is being managed (Pollack, 2004) would help sufferers and carers make choices and pave the way forward to making sure that that *choice will be available*. This may require a totally different political colour and direction to anything we have seen up until now!

## BIBLIOGRAPHY AND REFERENCES

Amminger, GP et al. (2010) Long-chain omega-3 fatty acids for indicated prevention of psychotic disorders: A randomized, placebo-controlled trial. *Archives of General Psychiatry, 67*(2):146–54.

Beebe, B & Lachman, FM (2002) *Infant Research and Adult Treatment. Co-constructing interactions* (Ch 5). London: The Analytic Press.

Bion, WR (1967) *Second Thoughts: Selected papers on psychoanalysis*. London: Maresfield Reprints.

Castellanos, FX et al. (1996) Quantitative brain magnetic resonance imaging in Attention-Deficit Hyperactivity Disorder. *Archives of General Psychiatry, 53*, 607–16.

Edelman, GM (1992) *Bright Air, Brilliant Fire: On the matter of mind*. Harmondsworth: Penguin.

Gallagher, S (2004) Article on fatty acids in pregnancy. www.midwiferytoday.com.

Hemmings, G (1989) *Inside Schizophrenia: A new comprehensive guide for sufferers and their families.* London: Sidgwick & Jackson.

Horrobin, D (2001) *The Madness of Adam and Eve.* London: Bantam Press.

Horrobin, D (2002) Cardiovascular disease, affective disorders and impaired fatty acid phospholipid metabolism. In E Chiu, D Ames & C Katona (eds). *Vascular Disease and Affective Disorders* (pp. 75–95). London: Martin Dunitz Press.

Khan A, Khan SR, Leventhal, R & Brown, WA, (2001) Symptom reduction and suicide risk among patients treated with placebo in antipsychotic clinical trials: An analysis of the Food and Drug Administration database. *American Journal of Psychiatry,158*(9):1449–54.

Koelsch, S, Kasper, E, Sammler, D, Schulze, K, Gunter, T & Friederici, A (2004) Music, language and meaning: Brain signatures of semantic processing. *Nature Neuroscience, 7*(3), 302–7.

Lawton G (2008) A game to train your brain? *New Scientist* (pp. 26–9), 12th January.

Manschreck, TC (ed) (2003) Nature and significance of soft neurological signs in schizophrenia. *Psychiatric Annals, 33*(3). (See especially pp. 157–66, 170–6, 181–7. The whole journal is given over to soft signs and Manschreck is the guest editor.)

Martin, S, Martin, E, Santoch, SR, Richardson, MA & Royall R (2001) Brain blood flow changes in depressed patients treated with interpersonal therapy or venlafaxine hydrochloride. *Archives of General Psychiatry, 58*(7), 641–8.

McFarlane, WR, Lukens, E, Link, B, Dushay, R, Deakins, S, Stasny, P, Newmark, M & Toran, J (2000) Employment outcomes in family-aided assertive community treatment. *American Journal of Orthopsychiatry, 70*(2), 203–14.

McFarlane, WR (2001) Family-based treatment in prodromal and first episode psychosis. In T Miller et al. (eds) *Early Interventions in Psychotic Disorders,* (pp.197–230). Dordrecht, NL: Kluwer Academic Publishers.

Peet, M (2002) Essential fatty acids: Theoretical aspects and treatment implications for schizophrenia and depression. *Advances in Psychiatric Treatment, 8*: 223–9.

Peet, M (2003) Dietary fat and schizophrenia. In M Peet, I Glen, DF Horrobin (eds) *Phospholipid Spectrum Disorder in Psychiatry (2nd ed).* Carnforth: Marius Press.

Peet, M, Brind, J, Ramachand, CN, Shah, S & Vankar, GK (2001) Two double-blind placebo-controlled pilot studies of eicosapentaenoic acid in the treatment of schizophrenia. *Schizophrenia Research, 49*, 243–51.

Peet, M & Horrobin, D (2002) A dose ranging exploratory study of the effects of ethyl-eicosapentaenoate in patients with persistent schizophrenic symptoms. *Journal of Psychiatric Research, 36*, 7–18.

Pollock, A (2004) *NHS plc: The privatisation of our health care.* London and New York: Verso.

Puri, BK & Richardson, AJ (2003) Long-term follow up of a single patient with schizophrenia treated with Ethyl–EPA alone. In M Peet, I Glen & DF Horrobin (eds). *Phospholipid Spectrum Disorder in Psychiatry (2nd ed)* (pp. 377–89). Carnforth: Marius Press.

Puri, BK, Richardson, AJ, Horrobin, DF, Easton, T, Saeed, N, Oatridge, A, Hajnal, JV, & Bydder, GM (2000) Eicosapentaenoic acid treatment in schizophrenia associated with symptom remission, normalisation of blood fatty acids, reduced neuronal membrane phospholipid turnover and structural brain changes. *International Journal of Clinical Practice, 54*(1), 57–63.

Richards, J (1993) Cohabitation and the negative therapeutic reaction. *Psychoanalytic*

*Psychotherapy, 7*(3), 223–39.

Richards, J (2001) What does psychosis have to say about racism? *Journal of the British Association of Psychotherapists, 39*, 1–15.

Schore, AN (1994) Socialization procedures and emergence of shame. In AN Schore, *Affect Regulation and the Origin of the Self.* Hillside, NJ: Lawrence Erlbaum.

Schore, AN (2002) Dysregulation of the right brain: A fundamental mechanism of traumatic attachment and the psychopathogenesis of posttraumatic stress disorder. *Australian and New Zealand Journal of Psychiatry, 36*, 9–30.

Sinason, M (1993) Who is the mad voice inside? *Psychoanalytic Psychotherapy, 7*(3), 207–21.

Sinason, M (1999) Jealousy and envy, green-eyed monsters or unrecognised switches of identity? Talk given at ISPS Conference, 16/17 September.

Tanskanen, A, Hibbeln, JR, Tuomilehto, J, Uutela, A, Haukkala, A, Viinmaki, H, Lehtonen, J & Vartiainen, E (2001) Fish consumption and depressive symptoms in the general population in Finland. *Psychiatric Services, 52*(4), 529–31.

Winnicott, DW (1976) The maturational processes and the facilitating environment. In DW Winnicott, *Ego Distortion in Terms of the True and False Self* (p.145). London: The Hogarth Press and The Institute of Psychoanalysis.

## Author's note

This chapter comes with gratitude to Georgie Wakefield whose enthusiasm knows no bounds and who, with her husband Paul, have inspired people to think more deeply about psychoses and what sufferers and carers have to tolerate.

It also comes with *profound* gratitude to all the patients I have ever had. I have learned the most important things from them.

## Abbreviations

*AA* – arachidonic acid

*AC LAT* – enzyme in the PLA2 cycle, that enables HUFA-CoA to be linked back to LyPL to make the phospholipid with fatty acid restore back to middle position

*DHA* – docosahexaenoic acid

*EPA* – eicosapentaenoic acid

*FA* – fatty acid

*FACL* – fatty acid coenzyme A ligase

*Omega-6 fatty acids* (from evening primrose etc.) – linoleic a to gamma linolenic to dihomogammalinolenic a to arachidonic a adrenic to docosapentaenoic

*Omega-3 fatty acids* (from fish oil) – alpha linolenic a to stearidonic to eicosatetraenoic a to eicosapentaenoic a (EPA) to docosapentaenoic to docosahexaenoic a (DHA)

*PLA2* – phospholipase A2

# 13

# Seeing the Wood for the Trees

It was explained to us that during therapy Christian might experience some symptom breakthrough because therapy tends to churn up thoughts and emotions, and that we should expect him to get worse before he gets better. He did experience some, but compared to what he has gained we feel that the alternative is far more daunting.

This is also helping him to accept his illness after all of these years and for the first time ever, instead of bottling things up, he has started to talk about what it's like when the 'other mind' kicks in. Rather than closing right off and suffering this torment alone, we discuss what is going on and he feels able to move on, rather than let it go round and round his head for hours on end.

We are all working together at last. I've written this poem to help you to try to imagine what it's like when the psychotic process is in charge and how TOM (Christian's name for his 'other mind') is the more powerful of the two minds ...

THE 'OTHER MIND'

I want to get close to people, my 'other mind' says no
My healthy mind tries to engage, but it's not strong enough and though
I want to live a normal life, my 'other mind' won't allow
My healthy mind tries to engage
But it doesn't quite know how
To fight off the powerful 'other mind' that rules with rods of steel
Dictating every move I make, predicting how I feel
I want to challenge the 'other mind', but my healthy mind is weak
The 'other mind' just shouts it down when it decides to speak
I want to join the world, but the 'other mind' holds me back
It controls my life with ease, my emotions on a rack
How can I conquer the 'other mind'? Strip it of its hold
Allowing my healthy mind some choice so normality unfolds
Through therapy I'll learn and grow until at last I find
A way to overpower it and erode
The 'Other Mind'

We were also warned that the 'other mind' would definitely protest against being disempowered, and would object by causing Chris even more problems. Again we have seen this but live in hope that one day his healthy self will get stronger.

An example is that today he thought that the people on the TV were telling him to go back to his flat. He said, 'I hate being alone Mum and I refuse to give in to it' – what a breakthrough! Instead of trying to deal with this alone, he spoke to me about it. I said, 'Well the "other mind" wants you to go home.' He said, 'I'm not going to and whenever this happens to me, I will tell you about it from now on and we will sort it out between us.' And so within a few weeks he was feeling able to discuss what's going on and find ways to deal with something that constantly insists on ruling his life.

Dianne also explained that we shouldn't get angry with the other mind because in its own way it is trying to 'protect and keep safe' and when you think about this logically, if we never went out into the world, and if we didn't ever chance having relationships, (which all too often can cause emotional pain), we would be far less likely to get hurt.

Consequently, someone who is so very sensitive is far safer and less likely to become ill if they live an extremely *'limited life'*, as most people with psychosis are forced to do by their other mind keeping them safe. Looking back, I can see exactly how hard life has been for my son. When he was only 18, he would try really hard to mix with young people. I can remember him saying that when he was out in a pub with a few old school mates, the hallucinations and voices had got so bad that he ran outside. One of them came out to him but he said that he couldn't talk to him about what was wrong. I have even known him to go to a local disco on his own. Paul found this extremely painful – how much easier it would have been for all of us to understand what was happening to him had we known this years before.

On 15th October, Christian came to the Civic Awards Ceremony. There were 22 people in our group – all family and friends and 400 people attended the event. He had a great time, he danced all night and we didn't get home until 1.30am! He went to work on Monday but by Tuesday his spirits had dropped dramatically. He started to complain about having a headache and a sore throat, but there was no sign of a cold. Previous to all of this, he had been going to MIND and had even been doing some gardening. He told me that he was making some friends there and that he was determined to keep this up. On Wednesday he didn't go in to work and came up to my place and got into bed complaining yet again of aches and pains, sore throat, headache, etc. We went out for some medication and although he was taking Beechams Powders, there was still no sign of a cold or flu. The only way I can describe the feelings that I had about it is that it reminded me of when he was a child and he wanted to get out of going to school, especially when they had a PE lesson – this had happened many times in the past. During the evening, he kept complaining. He said that when he'd walked up to my place, people were laughing at him as they went past in their cars. Even though I tried to convince him that it was the 'other mind', he wasn't convinced at all and argued with me. He heard me make a remark to his dad, when Paul said, 'What's wrong with Christian?' I replied, 'Oh it's TOM' and he came out of the bedroom and said I was stupid and that they really had laughed at him. We could both see that there was no point in arguing with him and so we dropped the subject. When he attempts to go out into the world, TOM intervenes and causes him problems, e.g. 'the people going past in their cars are laughing at you' and so the harder he tries to branch out, the more symptoms he will have to deal with. Sometimes he'd say that the voices came from the wheels of cars going by.

Last night I asked him, 'Are you pleased that Dr Lefevre has taught us all about the "other mind"?' He replied, 'Yes, very and I wish we had known about it a long time ago.' This is how Paul and I feel too – we could have been working with Christian. This understanding has helped all of us; I now feel that we should to be telling other carers about it so that, instead of the whole family becoming both totally confused and overwhelmed by the 'other mind', they too will have something to work with. Yesterday, Chris was watching TV when he came out into the kitchen and said that the people on TV were picking up his thoughts again. He said, 'How do they know what I am thinking?' I replied, 'Do you really think that they do?' After a very short pause he said, 'No Mum, I can see that it's just something that happens to me sometimes and I have to realise that sometimes it can catch me out. It's as if someone is playing games with me.' He went on, 'I will master it. I just have to become more aware and tell you about it so that we can work it out together.' We believe that he is only just coming to terms with schizophrenia and accepting that he has to find ways to deal with the symptoms.

Allow me to introduce you to TOM ...

**TOM**

Tom gets me to stay with him he wants to keep me safe
If I go beyond his boundaries, he dictates how I behave
Tom wants me to live a life of total isolation
Even though my healthy self is fuelled with sheer frustration
If I attempt to venture out, Tom feels he must object
My healthy self gets angry and feels the sad effect
Tom tells me that they laugh at me as they drive past me in their cars
As if I'm an ugly alien that's landed here from Mars
Tom doesn't mean to be so cruel, he thinks this is for my sake
He thinks he should protect me and watch each move I make
But my healthy self is lonely and craves some company
Tom just won't allow it, he will not set me free
But Tom is very frightened, perhaps he thinks I might get lost
Perhaps he thinks someone could hurt me, he doesn't think about the cost
The cost is far too painful, Tom should consider that
No one ever visits, but it says welcome on my mat
Tom's thumb sits firmly on my head, I'm his sad subservient clone
I want to do so many things but it's no fun on your own
Although I understand his motives and though Tom is part of ME
I so wish Tom would let me go and allow me to be free

Paul and I are now able to stand back and instead of getting angry with him, we talk to him about it. Sometimes he can see what's going on and other times he can't. When he can't, we simply drop the subject because he is totally overwhelmed by TOM and keeping on would simply make matters worse. Sometimes he will realise after a few hours he talks about it and is relieved. Recently, there have been times when he can see what's happening straight away but, considering that this is all still very new, I am very optimistic about the future and I am hoping that in time he will be able to realise what's happening very quickly and then move on.

Now for an easy way to understand the smaller but healthy process (mind) so let's meet TIM – 'Tormented Insecure Mind'.

**TIM**

My tormented insecure mind is known to me as TIM
TIM's weak and very sensitive and petrified of him
TIM is very pliable, he gives in to TOM's regime
The life TIM really wants to live is merely but a dream
TIM's weakness tends to sicken him
He's aware he should be strong

But he knows he'll pay the highest price
Should he dare to confront TOM
Because TOM has all the power, he holds the one ace card
TOM ridicules TIM's objections
Knowing he can make life hard
 So TIM plumps for isolation, like a prisoner in a cell
TOM thinks this is best for TIM and ignores the inner hell
TIM's desperate for some freedom, his life is so unkind
He has to find the strength to erode THE OTHER MIND ...

Recently, about eighteen months into therapy, we were at my mum's and we had arranged for Paul, Chris and me to meet Steve and Angela in the pub in Orsett Village at 8pm. Chris got very anxious and said that he was tempted to go home and the people going past in their cars were telling him to go home too. He was angry and said that it was hard to sit still. I talked to him about the 'other mind' and that it was TOM that was telling him to go home. At first he got even angrier and would not accept that it was TOM but, after a while he came round and could see what was happening and he decided that he would come out for a drink after all. Can you see the difference that understanding TOM and TIM has made within a short while?

During the filming of 'Loving Christian' there's a scene where Chris is talking to me. He keeps saying, 'I will have to go home now because people out there (pointing to the window) are telling me that I should and that I shouldn't stay here with you Mum.' This is what the 'other mind' was telling him at that time. I tried to reason with him and reassure him that it was OK to stay at our place, but after a while he said, 'It's no good I will have to go home.' – TOM HAD WON. Also during the filming, he described being in the grip of the 'other mind' as similar to being taken over by aliens. We are extremely grateful for the help Chris has been given and also what this therapy has taught us.

How can we possibly expect sufferers to cope without talking therapy to guide them through the maze of psychosis? For years we knew that Chris desperately needed someone to talk to him to help him to see the wood for the trees – explain what was happening to his mind and his life. Somehow I knew that even though it might be painful for him, he desperately needed help to unravel his thoughts and emotions. We enquired about talking therapies, but we were told that the waiting list was as long as your arm and as I explained earlier, we found a private counsellor but it was £30 a week out of his benefits and his reluctance to go after about five sessions took its toll and it died a death.

I've written this because I do not think that medication alone is anywhere near enough; tending the plant above root level when the problem lies beneath the earth is not sufficient. I am pleased to say that Christian has met the person who will help him to find himself and that person is Gwen Simpson, his art therapist, who also talks to him during his sessions about the 'other mind' – what we are learning is the importance of talking therapies simply because we can see the difference that it's making.

## CARE IN THE COMMUNITY

When the decision was made to introduce 'care in the community' there was obviously a total lack of understanding. Many people saw this as a positive move by the government but many service users and carers feel (as I do) that all they have produced is mini-institutions and lots of people are even more isolated.

As much as we all wanted to see the back of the asylums, no thought was given to the alternative ...

MINI-INSTITUTIONS
Sat up in their ivory towers
They designed this brilliant scheme
But none of them knew what was needed
Though service users and carers screamed
Let's knock down the institutions they said
We've got a far better plan
Life will improve for all of you
Every woman – every man
Folk will be kind, they'll welcome you
Just you wait and see
Incarceration's a thing of the past
Like caged birds you'll all be set free
You'll all be well supported they said
There's loads of support out there
But reality was different
Nobody seemed to care
Social exclusion prevailed
Social inclusion didn't exist
Our neighbours purely added us on

To a very long stigmatised list
Responsibility was placed at the carer's door
But carers had very few choices
We knew instinctively what would happen
But nobody heard our voices
New homes became institutions
Just smaller ones than before
Isolation and loneliness
Then back through the revolving door
They didn't feel our frustration
They didn't feel our rage
We were still imprisoned
We were still birds in a cage
A total lack of understanding
Reared its very ugly head
Filling our souls with foreboding
Anxiety sadness and dread
They hadn't thought it through you see
They thought they had all the solutions
We searched for care in the community
We found mini-institutions

# 14

# Welcome Home Christian

Stigma is a massive problem and until I feel confident enough to say 'my son suffers from schizophrenia' without the fear of ignorance, I will never rest. I want to be able to say this word without seeing that look of confusion and fear on people's faces.

I have always told Christian to be very proud of himself, and that it's not him who needs to change but public attitudes.

Do you ever question why the old institutions had such high walls built around them? I think (due to what you're about to read) it was to protect those inside. Thankfully we are chipping away but there is still a mountain to climb ...

**OUR FIRST ENCOUNTER ...**

Just before Chris moved into his flat, 100 residents (his new neighbours), staged a protest at the local junior school across the road. They sent letters to the local paper saying that they objected to the mentally afflicted living near to both them and the junior school.

I ask you now to bear in mind that our son had been living away from home for almost five years and he'd also been to hell and back. Christian read the letters and he found it really difficult to understand why these people would object to him living there, especially as they didn't even know him or any of the other young people who were moving in.

Persons unknown smashed the security lights around the flats on the night they moved in, which is something that none of these young people would even dream of doing. My thoughts? How dare these people believe they can act as judge and jury? HOW DARE THEY BELIEVE THEY CAN JUDGE HIM?! People, who don't know my son or my family, think they have the divine right to judge him and others purely because they don't know the first thing about this condition. How dare they accuse him of having an ulterior motive for being in a swimming pool with children, when he had simply gone there to swim (you are about to read about this).

I don't think we will ever recover from the feelings of disgust and sadness. As we all know young people tend to be very secretive, especially with their parents.

Christian knew that he was becoming ill for some time before he confided in us. He says that he wanted to tell us, but he knew that it was serious and didn't want to worry us – had he been taught about mental illness at school would he have talked to us earlier? Maybe he would have had far more insight into what was happening to him.

Teachers need to learn about what signs to look out for so that they can alert parents. Education sessions in schools would mean that both pupils and teachers would be aware of early warning signs. The benefits of this would be two-fold – firstly they would access services early and we all know how important that is and it would also enhance understanding and help to reduce stigma.

This poem helped me to deal with my feelings ...

### THE GRIM REAPER

How dare they believe they can judge him
When they don't even know his name
If they had any idea of his journey
They would hang their heads in shame
Judge and jury with misguided beliefs
Not one of them knows the truth
They judge the label he's forced to wear
Pinned on his misspent youth
Almost five years in rehab, fighting each day to stay sane
So bravely he's fought the demons time and time again
Distorted by the tabloids and the sensational stories they read
Adding fuel to the embers of prejudice
Whilst fulfilling the businessman's greed
How long will injustice reign?
Creating a living hell
Yet if this were a physical illness, sweet
Compassion, poor lamb's not well
Not one ounce of praise for their strength
With abuse they are more often met
No cards, no flowers, no comforting words
They fight the grim reaper and yet

It's time for some recognition; compassion's too long overdue
So dig deeply within your resources because one day this could be you

Recently another carer told me that while her son went out for a pizza his flat was set on fire – his crime? Schizophrenia and even though the family had tried hard to keep his diagnosis a secret, the secret got out and his flat was so badly damaged and he was so terrified that he became ill again and had to go back onto the wards. This tragic incident was just what a young man who is already terrified of the world around him needed!

We all know that early intervention is imperative to recovery. Many ideas are passed down by parents/peers – educational packs need to be placed in schools, colleges, youth centres, etc., this way you are educating before the rot sets in and it's the only way to ensure that attitudes will change.

### ENIGMA

Schizophrenia, madness, insanity, or condition lacking humanity?
Desperate for understanding, starving for support carers soldier on
Tired, anxious and totally stressed, the threads of pleasure long gone
But let's not talk about it, talking is not allowed
With the alienation of a leper we stand alone in a crowd
Though sadness and shame lace disbelief throughout each waking day
Compassion and understanding rarely comes our way.
The sufferers deserve some justice, recognition for their strength
Carers need support for the way their lives are spent
Can we dissolve these misconceptions stuck so hard to us like glue?
Dispersing fear and ignorance that makes it so taboo
Our shame is born of prejudice; our secrecy is born of stigma
We must tear down all the barriers creating this enigma

### OUR SECOND ENCOUNTER

Around six months after Chris moved into his flat, he decided he'd like to go swimming (before he became ill, he loved to swim). We were really pleased because we all know that physical exercise improves our mental health.

He was going swimming three times a week for about an hour each time. One day he came home and said that one of the lifeguards had commented on how often he went there. I have a friend who goes every day and I asked him what he'd replied. He said, 'I told him that I was trying to get over a mental illness and how I'd spent years in bed.' Alarm bells immediately rang for me, but Paul said, 'Perhaps he was just being friendly.' I had this nagging gut feeling that something was going to kick off.

A few days later Chris rang me at work. At first I didn't realise that it was him because he was shivering and crying at the same time. He kept repeating, 'Why did they keep asking me about children Mum?' To my horror it then transpired that two uniformed police officers had called him out of the pool and asked him why he was in there while there were children in there. Paul picked me up from work and we went to see the leisure centre manager who told us, 'It wasn't me, it was a head teacher who had felt it necessary to call the police.' We went to see her at a local junior school. I asked he, 'What promoted you to call the police about my son?' She said, 'I'm here to protect children.' I asked her, 'From what?' She repeated, 'I am here to protect children', and I repeated, 'From what? What exactly was my son doing?' She replied, 'He sort of stands at the side of the pool for ten minutes.' I explained that Chris sometimes has a job to make a decision about whether or not to stay in or get out. It was blatantly obvious that the lifeguard had told the manager that Chris had a mental illness. The manager told him to question Christian, and Christian in his innocence had told the truth. This was in turn relayed to the head teacher and all hell had broken loose. I said that if my son had been sitting in a wheelchair staring at the children, no action would have been taken. He had made the huge mistake of telling the lifeguard, 'I have a mental illness'. When the police came to see me, they openly admitted that they knew very little about schizophrenia, even though they are often the first on the scene when someone is experiencing their first psychotic breakdown. Christian refused to go swimming for the next ten months. When I suggested he went, he'd say, 'I can't go, I feel ashamed.' The incident affected him so badly that he became very depressed and was prescribed Prozac.

At the beginning of this book I said that readers would understand why I felt it necessary to take part in Rethink's DVD – they re-enacted the swimming pool incident and we can only hope that this campaign has at least some impact on public understanding.

Another carer whose son went to buy himself a cup of tea at a school fete was told by the lady behind the counter, 'We don't want your sort in here.' She also refused to serve him – this has to stop! They tell us that stigma is improving and I apologise for sounding so negative, but I think not.

Comment from a CPN who has worked in mental health for 21 years which includes 12 years on forensic wards, 'I have only ever been attacked once in all these years and that was by a nurse, not a patient!'

## OUR THIRD ENCOUNTER: AS BAD AS IT GETS

A while ago, I was conducting a presentation and there were around 40 people in the audience. Before I went on, the young man who delivers the service user perspective asked me if I would mind if he stayed for my slot. He seemed very nervous and at that moment in time I had no idea why as normally he was quite calm. The audience was varied – admin workers, porters, nurses and two psychiatrists. After talking for about 35 minutes, we moved onto questions and answers – people asked various questions and someone always asks how is Chris coping now. One woman was very concerned as her 23-year-old daughter had recently been diagnosed with schizophrenia and although she was living in her own flat, she wasn't managing very well.

At the end, a young man stood up and said, 'I don't have any questions but there is something I want to say to you. I am one of the demonic doctors you have been referring to ...' (my only reference to doctors was that I felt that consultants need to engage with carers far more and not hide behind a smoke screen of patient confidentiality). He went on, 'I thought your presentation was totally one-sided. We've heard about how terrible things have been for your son and your family, but what about all the terrible things your son has done to other people?' When I replied that my son had never done anything terrible to anyone, he said, 'We've only got your word for that.'

Afterwards I had a conversation with the service user and he explained he had stayed behind because he had had a very similar experience. This young man works tirelessly to improve matters. He'd been asked by this doctor, 'What are you doing to help the people who have been injured by people with mental illnesses?' At first I felt that this mountain was becoming far too hard to climb, but in time I realised that this unfortunate incident clearly highlights the desperate need for education. In this case it was not just a member of the public, but a professional – he was a psychiatrist in learning difficulties. I was assured that this would be dealt with and true to their word it was. Sadly, although the matter was dealt with, I will never forget my feelings of disgust and utter disbelief that a psychiatrist of all people could be so ill-informed and, even worse, that he could be so arrogant.

Carers and service users are often forced to tell lies. We become experts at covering up the truth because we are far too frightened of the reaction that the truth will be met with. I've also met carers who have lied to close family members – one father said, 'I can't tell my brothers. They have young children and the truth would worry them.' He seemed to feel ashamed to explain schizophrenia. Some carers aren't willing to use their real names in published articles and this is where we (the people who do know), must say enough is enough!

Our car number plate is P900 SOS – the P is for Paul because he has driven miles to conferences all over the country – the SOS is for Spotlight On Schizophrenia. Sometimes I'm asked does that stand for 'Save Our Souls'? and I tell them what it stands for. I then ask, 'Do you know much about this condition?' Nine times out of ten the answer is, 'No, not really', and then I tell them what they need to know and they end up wishing that they had never asked!

# 15

# The Soul Reason for Being a Carer

WHAT'S IT LIKE BEING A CARER? EXHAUSTING TO SAY THE LEAST
But carers don't have much choice, it's the nature of the beast!
What's it like being a carer? We're no longer in control
We're shell shocked, grieving, disbelieving, it bores into your very soul
There's all of the practicalities, we're forever on the phone,
Sorting out DSS benefits – running an extra home.
We wait very patiently through answer phones playing weird tunes
To be answered by someone who has no idea about what we're going
    through
What's it like being a carer?
We grieve for what would have been
His life lies shattered before him, mental illness stole every dream
What's it like being a carer? Mostly a thankless task
 But now and again we're rewarded when furtively they will ask
'Do you think I'm doing OK Mum?' 'Do you think I'm improving with
    time?'
'Of course you are' is the carer's reply; you're nearing the end of the line
We're never really sure about what the answer should be
We say what they need to hear, 'I'm right son, you take it from me'
What's it like being a carer? You long to be free from the chains
We get tired from watching them struggle, playing witness to so much
    pain
What's it like being a carer? You learn to accept your lot!
You can kick and scream forever more but a mental illness is what he's
    got!
We get sick of reassuring saying, 'Everything will be OK'
Tired from sorting out muddled minds day after day after day
Reassurance becomes our middle name, as we build on their confidence
We know instinctively if they're anxious, confused, depressed, or tense
There's messages in the inbox when we check the mobile phone
'Where are you Mum will you be long? I'm sick of being alone'
So why do we keep on caring, we're well aware that life should be fairer
That's simple the answer is love – The Soul Reason for Being a Carer

## WE ARE NOT ALONE: KEITH'S POEM

A carer rang me one evening; he was from Rotherham. Keith is a school caretaker at a local secondary school. He talked about how he cuts the huge lawns in the school grounds on a sit-and-ride mower. It's the school that his own son attended. He said that very often, the tears are streaming down his face. His son became ill at 14 and he had spent his 16th birthday on an acute ward – made even worse because it was Christmas time (2004). Through his tears he said, 'Do you know duck, I'd never read a book in my life but when I read "A Mother's Story", I found it hard to believe that someone else could feel as bad as I do.' He explained that the book had given him comfort and also strength just to know that someone else could be feeling and trying to deal with exactly the same pain. We talked about everything that he and his wife were going through. He had given the book to extended family members to read and he said that they understood the illness far better now. Keith told me that he decided to have the front cover of. 'A Mother's Story' tattooed on his arm. I thought he was joking, but about a week later a photo of Keith's arm came through the post!

Keith was talking to Paul one evening – it was just after he'd watched the documentary about Christian on TV. He said, 'Well I know what you look like now Paul, but you don't know what I look like – I could be sitting here in a dress for all you know!' Despite his heartache, Keith still tries to retain his sense of humour and one evening he said, 'I write poetry too you know Georgie, in fact I could read you one that I wrote the other night.' This is Keith's poem:

I saw a cow upon a 'ill
It ain't there now
So it must have gone!

Carers do find comfort in each other, which is why I often say that we need an early intervention service for carers preferably provided by old hands for new carers. I believe that had we had someone who totally understood what we were going through, that we could call on at more or less any time, it would have helped us both a great deal (once again lack of resources), especially a man for Paul to talk to. I've been able to let some of the pain out through writing but Paul still has loads inside (his precious garden does help). It shows in the documentary we made and screened at

9pm on the 5th October 2004. I was able to talk even about the bleak years without breaking down, whereas Paul broke down a few times, always apologising to the producer who was very understanding and supportive.

Getting back to our journey this will give you an idea about what the next two years were like, it was very similar to the first seven years, the wilderness years …

### A TYPICAL DAY OF NOTHINGNESS

The phone rings, its 9.30am. I'm up writing as usual I started about 7.10am. If only I could stop trying to improve things and be satisfied with what I've written.

'Hello Mum what are we doing today?'

'Well I need to work on my book Chris'

'What can I do then? It's too cold to go swimming and I get sick of going alone'

'How about doing some of your painting by numbers?'

'No I'm not in the mood today'

'You could go to MIND, there may be some young people there?'

'No Mum, last time I went it felt like the walls were caving in and most of them there are much older than me and sometimes I feel even more depressed when I go there. I get fed up with mixing with people who aren't well, I'd like friends who are well but how can I just find them it's not easy'

'How about doing some housework?'

'It doesn't need doing today'

'You could listen to some music'

'I'm sick of listening to music'

'Chris I can't find you things to do, you have to do that yourself'

'There's nothing, is there Mum? I try really hard but there's nothing, just long boring days. I see other people laughing together, enjoying their day and I'm just here with nothing to do and nowhere to go.

It starts to turn into an argument

'But what do you expect me to do? I've told you a million times I can't find friends for you. I can't find you things to do. I can't bloody well entertain you Chris!'

'I'll walk up to you then.' Phone goes dead.

I hear your key in the door ten minutes later.

'I feel really tired Mum, is it OK if I get in your bed to rest for a while?'

'Of course it is Chris, I'll just finish this paragraph and then I'll make us both a cup of tea, how does that sound?'

'Not for me Mum, I feel a bit sick like I've got butterflies in my stomach.

I'll try to sleep for a while.' It's 10.20am.

1.00pm. 'What time's dad home?'

'In about ten minutes Chris'

'What shall we do this afternoon then?'

'Do you fancy a walk around Lakeside?'

'If you like Mum, but there's not really anything I need'

'OK its better than just lying around here anyway'

At Lakeside, we walked around, aimlessly looking in shops for about thirty minutes when quite suddenly he said, 'Give me the car keys Mum, I'm going to have a cigarette. I'll wait in the car for you.' When I returned to the car, he said, 'It seems to me like everyone is being friendly to you, but not to me. A man went past the car and it felt like he was picking up my thoughts, he knew exactly what I was thinking, it was horrible.' I asked him, 'Does it seem as if your thoughts are being broadcast?' He replied, 'Yes and it's so very painful and I am so sick of it. Why does it keep happening to me? I shouldn't have to keep going through this, I haven't done anything wrong and yet I feel so guilty. It feels as if I am being punished, but for what? It's just not fair!'

There are times when there are no words that will bring him comfort. I become speechless even though I am searching my mind for the right thing to say, it just becomes stalemate; at this point I remain quiet.

Its 3.30pm and we're on our way home again. I am thinking that no wonder the suicide rate is so high, how much mental torture can one person take? Silence prevails for a while and then I say, 'Shall I drop you at MIND just for an hour, it would fill a little time for you and there must be someone to chat with?'

'No Mum, I'm not in the mood today let's just go home eh?'

I try hard to make conversation but you keep saying 'I don't feel like chatting, my head hurts'. It feels as if there's a band down the middle of your head which always gets worse if you try to look to the right. Your face is burning and you feel as if your blood pressure has gone up, especially in your head. You then say that the worst part of all is your lower arms, they feel so pumped up that it feels as if they will burst open. I'm now wondering if you will ever self-harm to relieve the tension. I decide to stop talking – that's the best way until the storm has passed – allow time to pass.

The storm does pass until the next time.

Home again.

'I'm going to lay down, I'm tired.'

'OK, I'll call you for your tea.'

'Don't put me much up Mum, I just don't fancy food. I never really enjoy food, did you know that?'

'No Chris I didn't.'

'Well I don't!'

'Fancy watching TV? I could bring the portable in for you.'

'No thanks, it does my head in sometimes. I feel as if the people on there are putting pressure on me.'

'But they're not Chris, it just feels like it to you.'

You eat a few mouthfuls of shepherd's pie and at about 8.15pm, Paul runs you home as you feel exhausted. Before you leave you tell us how you've been worried all day.

'What about Chris?'

'You and dad dying. I worry about that all the time.'

How can I not understand that – I totally understand it. We are his safety blanket. Sometimes I get so tired of the responsibility of being a carer and forever thinking what will happen when we are gone? What about my other son and my daughter-in-law and the burden that it will inevitably put on them? How will he be able to cope when the dog dies? My mum is 81, my sister is ill, what if something happens to them? Will he relapse?

Just another day in the life of a carer, with another following far too closely behind it ...

Recently we found we had a decision to make – I had been on and on about buying a puppy in case Chris were to be badly affected by our old dog, 'Jimmy', dying – at 13 we knew that his time was short. We went out and bought a Border Terrier pup, 'Rosie'. She was beautiful, but Jimmy did not approve and every time she did a small puddle, he would do one the size of a large dinner plate over the top of it. He also became quite aggressive towards her and snarled every time she tried to get near him. After a week of sheer hell, we sold her for exactly half of what we paid (£400) thinking 'big mistake, lovely pup, bad timing'. Three weeks later, our old dog was suddenly taken ill and died. At first we thought we won't have a dog, but we all missed Jimmy (especially Christian who so far hasn't cried, which is not really a good sign). Since Jimmy's death, he has not been at all well and this is probably why. Last week we bought another Border Terrier pup, a boy named 'Alfie'.

Christian is getting very frustrated because he has got more motivation now and he so wants to get out there and join the world, but having lost his social skills, he needs help. We are feeling very frustrated too because we are firm believers in the fact that you can't pigeon-hole people (regardless of whether they have a mental illness or not) and not everybody with a mental health problem wants to go to Mind, which is the only alternative. Chris can engage with people and he gets on really well with his befriender. I am unable to accept that he can't socialise, he is capable but it's by no means easy and he needs support; social inclusion has to be with the right people – only then will his confidence grow. He often says that mixing with other sufferers makes him feel sad and he wants to get away from mental illness, not get more involved in it! We both feel that no one really knows Christian. He will talk about his problems, but it has to be the right person that he is talking to and if only someone would go to see him on a regular basis and build up a relationship with him, it would help him such a lot ...

These short verses are to help people to see that very often the signs are there, and carers can see them ...

SOCKS
You're smiling today
No sign of a frown
But one sock's black
The other is brown

LINES
When you walked through the door
Everything was fine
At the drop of a hat
You're over the line

VOICES
You're looking startled
But you have no choices
Old enemies
Angry voices

CLOTHES
You've changed again
A blue top this time
Six times today
You've changed your mind

**FOOD**

Slowly you push your plate away
Don't fancy it Mum
No appetite today?

**WRONG**

Your back is stooped
Your postures wrong
You're looking so tired
You don't stay for long

**DREAMS**

Your eyes are dancing
You should have seen
The colours were vivid
In my dream

**FRUSTRATION**

You're so frustrated
Wringing your hands
I try to explain Mum
But you just don't understand

**NO DISGUISE**

When you're seeing things
There's no disguise
I see the fear
It's in your eyes

**NIGHTMARES**

It's as if I'm reliving these evil dreams
I repeat to myself
This is not what it seems

**FREEDOM**

You stare back at me so searchingly
Mum do you think I will ever be free?

**ENDLESS SLEEP**

This is a dream in my soul I'll keep
That the day will come you won't need endless sleep

**THOUGHTS**
I get too many thoughts surely that's wrong
Then my mind's blank and the thoughts are all gone

**AGITATION**
I feel agitated and I can't sit still
And why do I worry that my brother is ill?

**LOST**
Sometimes I wonder who I really am
Will I find myself do you think I can?

**HOPE**
You had an illness how did you cope
How on earth did you mange to hold on to hope?

**CONFUSION**
You look really tired Dad and so does Mum
Tell me the truth am I really your son?

A very unusual poem written by another carer:

**SPLIT**
Twenty-six years ago our son planted a conker
By the front door, yes by the door
Up it came like a fighter waving two flags
A bit of a joke to us (our son too)
Came a year when the joke turned serious
The tree demanded space room to grow up and out
(Our son too)
So we moved it away from the door
Allowed it to grow and spread
Took us a while to notice how odd it was
Several stems or trunks
Not the usual one
Going up like a normal tree
Several going out
It took us a lot longer to notice
The oddity of our son
Going this way and that
And no way at once
We reduced the stems to four

Symmetry seeming right
Our son's tangled courses
We failed to stop
Schizophrenia split our lives our son our hearts
Our hopes split us from others
Blacked out the sun
I hallucinated asked will he get better?
No was gently said
That doesn't happen
I saw a sword in the air
Scimitar shaped a little above my head
For days I saw the sword
Scimitar shaped and shining
Felt it slice
A piece of music joined it
Pipe music from the Andes
And the words
Doesn't happen doesn't happen
The sword sliced
The music pierced the words
Cut up my heart
Well to get back to the tree
We found it dull it grew
Yes it grew but never flowered
Or conkered just grew
Only exciting when
It raised a host of spears
Against the fires of sunset
The threat of winter
Or in spring when the leaves
Came rollicking out of their sheaths
Like boys out of school ready
To put on gloves and fight
Other than that it was pretty dull
Our son was pretty unchanging
Though we visited every day
To join him to life
Sometimes he lifted sometimes
Then sank again and was gone
Still we visited every day
To link him to life
But today April Thirteenth at breakfast time

I saw through the window a spire
A white spire
Out I ran and counted
Six no seven no eight
White spires on the chestnut tree
In bloom at last
Is it an omen?
I collect omens my Irish blood
My Scottish genes insist on omens
Our son is certainly better
Takes drugs that sew splits
Together can cope is merry
A huge improvement
But will he flower fruit?
Walk with the world have love?
Yes? No?
Well his tree is in flower
Its waiting time is done
We have a different tree
And a very different son

We all know that lack of understanding isn't helped by the fact that there is nothing to outwardly show when it comes to mental illness. Perhaps we need ...

A BRAIN IN A WHEELCHAIR
A deaf man wears a hearing aid
If you're crippled you have a chair
A blind man carries a white stick
We all look on and sympathise
We all say life's so unfair
Even if we're deaf and dumb
Sign language provides a clue
We often offer a helping hand
I feel sure this has happened to you
But with mental illness we're struck blind
There's nothing to visually show
There's no props to give us insight
No one would ever know
Is this why there's so little compassion?
And fewer people seem to care
If that's the case my question is

Is that really fair?
Small wonder carers feel sad
Dealing daily with hidden pain
Would it help if we bought a wheelchair
And in it we placed a brain?

# 16

# Tea and Sympathy

Over the years we have met many professionals, some have been totally dedicated and many are our close friends now. Sadly there will always be some mortgage payers who are more interested in what they earn than improving the quality of people's lives.

We need to work together in harmony, carers and professionals respecting each other for our individual but equally important expertise. If we can achieve this we will all reap the rewards. We are all in an extremely painful place, we all pass the parcel of shame. The shame starts with the service user who loses control of his or her life, carers feel shame due to public ignorance and professionals feel shame because there is only so much they can do due to lack of resources.

### TEA AND SYMPATHY OR A BAD ATTITUDE?

The following poem was written to try to explain the importance of having a good relationship between carer and professional. This particular day I was feeling very tired, very anxious and sick to death of the struggle. This was not about a clash of personality, it was about a professional who had no idea about how hard life is sometimes. When I voiced my frustration the reply was, 'I didn't know you wanted tea and sympathy.' Well, the answer to that is that there are many times that tea and sympathy are exactly what we do want ...

MAKING AMENDS

I find you so stand-offish, uncaring that's the word
You make me think I make a fuss, yet I know that that's absurd
I feel that I'm a nuisance and my problems don't exist
Yet another moaning carer to add to your long list
I find you so unfeeling, no comfort in my plight

Even when I'm desperate and exhausted by this fight
It's imperative you understand, the strain from day to day
The sadness that I feel inside, the times I lose my way
I feel sure that you are unaware of the effect you have on me
Perhaps I'm making too much fuss? I dare say you'd agree
I find that you're no help at all, unlike others in the past
They brought me so much comfort, their memories still last
Your role is so important, we need so much to be friends
But I find you so stand-offish and feel we'll never make amends

As in any job we need the ...

#### TOOLS OF THE TRADE
Diplomas, certificates, 'ologys, degrees,
Very admirable academics are clever
All of it learned from neatly bound books
But does this impress a carer? No never
A carer's impressed by a welcoming smile
A hug or a pat on the hand
A nurse willing to go that extra mile
Is the language that we understand
You can ditch your many textbooks
Imprinted and stamped on your brain
You will need a compassionate nature
To help us to deal with our pain
Kindness, compassion, humility
Can these qualities really be taught?
Or are they part of your personality
We all know they can't be bought
A carer's theory of mental health caring
Is centred around being kind
It's of the utmost importance
To a carer's well-trained mind
So dig deeply within your resources
Seek and you will find
If I'm asked what makes a good nurse?
That's simple I say 'Just Be Kind'

Another incident that springs to mind was when Chris was in an acute ward. A nurse said that he was displaying bad behaviour (at the worst he would raise his voice a little). What struck me more than anything was her lack of understanding. I pointed out that at the age of 23, my son should be lying on a beach abroad with a blonde and not on a mental health ward. I asked her did she expect him to be happy? After all who would be? It's strange how lack of understanding seems to weave a way through mental illness continually ...

## I MUST BE WORTHLESS

This next piece was provided by a service user who has had many spells in hospital and wanted to include what he felt was important to this book. These are his words:

*As in all professionals there is good and bad, but in this profession you must strive to find the naturals and dispense with the career pension seekers. I have seen the lowest form of worker on full-time staff doing most of the work and being more approachable than the higher or head nurses, whilst having to take the most responsibility and being paid less for their trouble. As a patient, client, service user, I've had to kick scream, fight, threaten (officially) and cajole for most of the services that I have received. Mystery patients would help to provide a better understanding. We are in hospital to heal, not to play politics with admin managers. Below I list some advice.*

1. *Staff that do their jobs properly should be recognised and appreciated regardless of their status.*
2. *Staff that do their jobs badly should be disciplined regardless of their status.*
3. *Listen to both patients and carers; they have the knowledge.*
4. *Improve on communication between departments; this causes stress to vulnerable patients.*

*An example of what happened to me!*
*Me: Excuse me nurse, I'm not doing so good (be it that I need to talk or that I'm full blown suicidal).*
*Nurse: OK, just give me a couple of minutes.*
*Me: It's been two hours, I think she's forgotten about me.*
*Oh well, that's about my lot in life, I must be worthless.*

## CARERS NEED HELP WITH HOPE

Without hope we are lost. I have written this to explain the difference a professional can make to the carer's life. The next two poems are about two professionals – one who took my hope away and the other who gave me hope. The professionals' words, whether negative or positive, will go around and around a carer's head for days. We are extremely receptive to what you say to us. I can't stress the importance of what professionals say to carers enough. A good professional can make such a difference just by carefully choosing the right words before they actually speak, or as they say 'engage your brain before engaging your mouth'.

We will start with the negative attitude first. When this happened, Paul was painting the lounge and I can remember saying, 'It's no good, I must ring that support worker back because she will keep doing this to other carers.' My thoughts were ...

HOPE ISN'T YOURS TO STEAL
He's refusing to go to the day centre
He just doesn't want to join in
But he's fighting a losing battle
It's a battle that he'll never win
(me) But it makes him more depressed to go
So what's the point in that?
Waves of frustration pour over me
My voice sounds depleted and flat
Well one day he'll have to go along
He'll get sick of being alone
Like all of the rest he'll go along
It does them good to get out of the home
At this point I look into the future
His dark hair has now turned grey
He's there just as she predicted
On a cold wet miserable day
My hand shakes as I put down the phone
I don't need her negativity
I compose myself and call her back
I have to make her see
I thought you were there to support me
But you're not a psychiatrist
Only God can predict my son's future

Very slowly she gets my gist
I didn't mean to upset you
But he relies far too much on you
We reach a curt strained agreement
I'm aware what she's saying is true
The moral of this story is to help a carer to cope
 Don't advise us to stare into the future
We must preserve our hope
Hope is so important, it predicts how we all feel
It's taken us years to preserve it
It's ours and it's not yours to steal.

And now for the other side of the coin and the difference that a few words from a good professional can make ...

SEEING THE LIGHT
I feel sure that Christian will make it
I cling on to what you say
Like sweet music to my grateful ears
If you knew how hard I pray
I can see him in his own flat
And I feel sure he'll work one day
Maybe only part time
I find the words and say
You don't know what that means to me
What you say preserves my hope
Others steal it from me
Then I find that I can't cope
Your words give me the reason
To fight another day
Through the maze of schizophrenia
Your words light up the way
So that I can see the exit
And see an end in sight
Through your confident, positive attitude
 I finally see the light

And basically it's about having confidence and being positive – the confidence that this nurse had helped me to cope with caring and I will always be grateful.

# 17

# Patient Confidentiality and High Expressed Emotion

Both can be very sore subjects, often causing conflict between professionals and carers. Information on the type of mental health problem that the person you care for has should be made available to you, along with guidance on its management. However with mental health professionals, it's their duty to keep personal information about their client confidential.

Mental health professionals are not permitted to disclose any personal information about the people they care for and treat to anyone, unless they are a member of the individual's care team or unless they have permission from the individual. You will not receive information about the person that you care for unless they have given permission. Any discussion that you have with the professional about the person that you care for should also be treated confidentially and would not be disclosed to the person you care for without permission.

If the person you care for wants to keep you informed they will need to state this in writing to the mental health team – the problem I had was that yet again I did not know this. The person you care for retains the right to change this decision at any time they wish and their wishes will be adhered to. If the person you care for lacks the capacity [temporary or permanently] to consent to information being shared, it will be up to their care team to consider whether or not it would be in his or her interests to discuss their care and treatment with you. If they expressed their wishes prior to losing their capacity to make this decision, those wishes should be followed.

Recently I was attending a Rethink conference and high expressed emotion was mentioned. This was followed by a wave of disapproval from the audience of carers. This is what happened when Chris was about 20. I had taken him for his appointment with his consultant and he'd not been at all well for weeks; he'd had lots of trouble sleeping and he was also experiencing lots of positive symptoms.

Paul waited in the car and I went in with him. His consultant asked him how he had been and to my amazement he replied, 'I'm fine thank you doctor'. I was so shocked that towards the end I asked the doctor if I could talk to him alone. The following poem explains what happened next which made me feel ...

### I'M OF NO IMPORTANCE

Doctor may I talk with you? I plead with him once more
Your son's the patient, is his response as we approach the door
I feel like screaming in his face, but you won't get the truth
He won't admit to voices but I remain aloof
I wonder if he understands what it's like to live with you
Does he think I make it up when every word is true?
The familiar giant wall appears unseen to the naked eye
Frustration sticks hard in my throat, I feel I want to cry
I'm encroaching on his territory, but it seems I have no right
Does he feel embarrassed to discuss our sorry plight?
But there's more to this than side effects, there's grief and isolation
There's a longing to be listened to that's fuelling my frustration
He's suspended way above my head, I crave his reassurance
But it seems I'm just your carer and I'm of no importance

When we got in the car the first thing Paul said was, 'Did you talk to the doctor?' I replied, 'No, he refused to listen to me.' Paul started shouting and said, 'So after weeks of hell, the doctor doesn't have a clue how bad things are and refuses to even listen to us, even though we are the ones trying to deal with this day in day out – oh well that's great.' He was raising his voice and getting very angry. My question is what did that 12-weekly visit do to help us with high expressed emotion?. Christian was very upset because we were arguing but we could not help ourselves and the situation did nothing at all for so-called ...

### HIGH EXPRESSED EMOTION

I detest this terminology, do you feel just the same?
As if we shouldn't show our feelings when our loved ones go insane
Expect expressed emotion – a carer's life's unkind I'm still haunted
Though 20 years have passed by since the day he lost his mind
I think you'll find it's different when someone's physically ill instead
But carers must keep a lid on things if the problem's in the head
This needs to be deleted it needs to be addressed
It needs to be fully understood 'Emotions Have To Be Expressed'

I could understand if Christian had objected to the doctor talking to us, but he never has. If the patient does object then their wishes should be respected, but surely if the patient doesn't, a couple of minutes to talk to the carers should be respected too. As for high expressed emotion I would like to know why it's perfectly acceptable to show emotion when someone we love is physically ill but if mental health carers show emotion, it's not acceptable.

## SOME POSITIVE COMMENTS I'VE HEARD OVER THE YEARS

Nurse ... 'A young man was dragged into our ward by two burly policemen. He was naked and covered in pink cream. He had a tin foil hat on his head. They were very rough with him. I told them to stand back. I held out my hand. He took my hand. I turned to the policemen and said, "It's as simple as that".'

Nurse ... 'She had a very wild look in her eyes. She lashed out at me. "You're in desperate need of a hug", I said. She allowed it.'

Nurse ... 'Both parents were totally exhausted and distraught. The mother was shaking and sobbing, "We'll soon settle him down. Would you both like a cup of tea?"'

Carer ... 'I'm afraid he's neglected himself recently, I've tried to encourage him to look after himself.'

Nurse ... 'You take yourself off home and rest, we'll soon have him smelling like a rose.'

## SOME NEGATIVE COMMENTS

Support worker to carer [me] ... [12 years into my son's illness] – 'Sad as it is, you must be getting used to it by now.' The truth is you never get used to it.

Support worker to carer ... [whose son was twisted up through a bad dystonic reaction and lying in a cot on an acute ward] – 'He's been like that all day, perhaps he's putting it on.'

GP to carer [me] ... [Chris was experiencing a dystonic reaction – bearing in mind I had no idea what was happening to him] 'For God's sake pull yourself together, get him over to A&E and they will zap him.'

Support worker to carer ... 'There's only one thing worse than a parent that doesn't care and that's one that cares too much.' Can we care too much?

Support worker to carer [whose son was living in supported housing] ... 'I've warned my own son about drugs, I told him, you don't want to end up living somewhere like the people who I look after.' [This was said to me and Christian was there too.]

Nurse to carer [whose son was going home following six months in hospital] ... 'He'll be back.'

This is the worst comment of them all: Nurse to carer/mother [about her son who was on an acute ward] ...'They can be very unpredictable you know, I mean if he decided to jump out of that window up there head first, he'd just go ahead and do it.' Unbelievable, but true!

## SALVAGING SUPPORT

Salvaging your own support could be done by explaining this condition to friends and family. If this were a physical illness we would discuss things, so why not when it's a mental illness? Well we all know the answer to that question – carers are frightened to admit that their son or daughter has schizophrenia because people don't understand! By getting as many family members as possible together right at the start, we can at least attempt to gather their support. If we become reclusive, we will drift apart or even worse fall out, I do know this from personal experiences.

Carers need to talk about things well before the rot sets in. There is nothing to be ashamed of. Teaching others will provide them with the understanding that they will need to be able to support you – unless you do this, you are at risk of losing people forever.

These are a handful of stories relayed to me over the years:

A carer whose brother refused to allow her daughter to come to his daughter's wedding in case she made a scene. This woman had been stable, and living independently for six years. In her own words, 'My brother and I haven't spoken since and yet we'd always been so close.'

A carer whose son used to help her best friend in her garden until he developed schizophrenia. When she asked why they no longer asked him over, they were told, 'We're far too busy' – end of relationship.

A carer who, even after a year, felt unable to disclose her son's diagnosis because her siblings would be scared as they had young children.

A carer whose neighbour asked her, 'What is he likely to do?' when she finally plucked up the courage to tell her.

A carer whose own mother was not even prepared to discuss her daughter's illness with her.

Carers whose husbands have accused them of mollycoddling their sons and walked out.

A carer who was petrified of her neighbours finding out and talking about her problems to other neighbours.

I have even met service users who have problems with their own parents, who accuse them of being lazy and not trying hard enough.

So get in first and hold your own family conference. Invite as many people as you can – those that refuse to come obviously don't care anyway – those that do are far more likely to support you afterwards.

Carers gradually learn to stand up for themselves and the person they are caring for, as we have to fight their corner for them.

I wrote this poem because I have often been amazed at the close bond between mental health carers. I was talking to a carer recently who said that when she joined a support group, her first thoughts were that she had nothing in common with the other carers and had it not been for the situation that she was in, she would not have chosen to mix with them socially. She said that she thought at first, 'OK we're all here for the same reason but that is as far as this goes', not realising that you form a bond because of the situation that you share. Now a year on, they are all firm friends who go out together socially on a regular basis. I am in touch with many other carers and we ring each other frequently.

**KINDRED SPIRITS AND UNITED SOULS**

Carers are kindred spirits
We feel each others pain
Our bond is almost tangible
As we desperately try to stay sane
Carers are there for each other
Every second, day or night
Providing a shoulder to cry on
In our endless painful plight
Carers are often weary, anxious and terrified
We lose sight of a normal existence
We lose count of the tears we have cried
Carers rely on each other
Which is why we become so close
Empathy provides the bonding
During times when it's needed the most
Every carer understands
The sheer grind of the caring role
Carers – kindred spirits; carers – united souls

# 18

# Understanding Through Poetry

Unless you've suffered from mental distress it's hard to imagine how painful life can be. The next poem is about the empathy between myself and a friend who suffers with bipolar disorder, he is the strongest person I have ever met …

**HOW LONG?**
The umbilical cord of mental distress
I know yours and you know mine
'Don't call me, I need time alone' you say
Isolation reigns sublime
You're aware that I won't disturb you
Truly I don't feel offended
The Bionic Man has fallen apart
Given time and space he'll be mended
I don't wonder what you're doing
Or how long this silence will last
I just pray to God you stay strong
As you've had to do in the past
I marvel at your courage
After so many painful falls
You're dogged determination
Locked behind such lonely walls
You force yourself to get up out of bed
Clean the house and go to the shop
Force yourself to go to the gym
Though the voice of exhaustion screams stop!
I've immense respect for your suffering
So hard, so sad, so deep
Your tenacity astounds me
Night after night with no sleep
The silence of the unused phone
Deafening but I understand

I'm powerless to help your plight
Or steady your trembling hand
You remind me of a chameleon
Such a toughened outer skin
But inside hides a delicate child
With a pain so deep within
The umbilical cord of suffering
You know mine and I know yours
The world hurries past your window
But you're safe behind closed doors
Hold onto your qualifications
Unleashed talent so bitter to taste
They say time and tide waits for no man
But this time out won't go to waste
For now you have to be patient
You and I both know this will pass
One thing we're never sure of
Is 'How Long?' isolation will last

**LIVING ON A KNIFE EDGE** (Written by my friend, Mathew V Morrisey)
Living on a knife edge
Feelings like razors
Unable to relax
Feels like a gun to my head
Anxiety like a freight train
Running through my veins
Nothing can stop me talking
A mad man again
Nothing can make me total
Driven by my nerves
The train is running without tracks
My heart is pounding
Heading for a heart attack
The world of form is invisible
My mind like a live wire
Put my brain on ice
It never seems to tire
Reaching out to others
No one can help
Insulation gone
Like a live wire
Someone pull me down to earth

Can't you see that I'm on fire?
Nothing can quench my thirst
No one can reach me
You believe I'm normal
I'm not sure who's the liar!!!

## MY OWN THOUGHTS ON VARIOUS CONDITIONS

Self-harm is very misunderstood, I have talked to patients who have even had problems with professionals. A young girl I know was told by a nurse, 'You're just seeking attention, but I can assure you, you won't get it from me!' Another was refused blood by a doctor following a suicide attempt. I wrote this poem after lengthy conversations with a young woman about why she self-harms, she'd had a dreadful childhood ...

### A DAY IN THE LIFE OF AN AVID SELF-HARMER
I don't understand her or why she self-harms
Just look at the state of her legs and her arms
They whisper in corners, they stare at my scars
As if I'm an alien that's landed from Mars
The temptation to cut is always there
To relieve my feelings of utter despair
A voice in my head screams cut go on cut
Year in and year out I'm still stuck in this rut
The blade sinks so easily into my skin
Sweet relief from the pain I'm constantly in
Endorphins swim through my tired brain
But it's easy to cope with the physical pain
Attention-seeker I hear them say
Unaware of the struggle day after day
My negative feelings load every dice
An innocent child paid the highest price
I'm locked in a cupboard under the stairs
Nobody hears me, nobody cares
Through the years of abuse when I was a child
The perpetrator's amazement when I became wild
I imagine a mother loving, serene
I wake with a start it's only a dream
I pray for sleep, I pray for peace
I stare at the ceiling, there is no release

I reach for the blade, temptation's too strong
I'm filled with disgust, they tell me it's wrong
The blood oozes out and in an instant I'm calmer
Just one day in the life of an avid self-harmer

## SUFFERING TOURETTE'S

Fuck-shit-bugger they all stand and stare I'm desperate to crawl in a hole
I spit, I tick, I pull grimacing faces, I'm totally out of control
It's like being tempted all of the time, but you just can't resist the temptation
People stare, they call me names, the shame, the humiliation
If I ever find a partner will she never understand?
Tourette's is extremely painful, not exactly what I'd planned
Fuck-shit-big tits I'm off again, chaos is my closest friend
Nigger-fucker-knickers-dicks – will this hell ever end?
A gang held me down the other day, they washed my mouth out with soap
My mates all fell by the wayside, far too embarrassed to cope
He's just like an animal, nutter they say, let's take him down to the vet's
If only they could understand what it's like to cope with Tourette's

## 123 OCD

123 OCD 456 mind plays tricks 789 and 10
The fear starts mounting yet again
He taps the counter, taps the floor
100 times and then some more
Before he left home this morning, he continually washed his hands
It's all so time consuming, he finds it so hard to make plans
He's tormented by his rituals, they rule his life day and night
He wonders how long he can cope, or keep up the strength for the fight
His wife gave up and left him, she felt she'd taken too much
He told her not to feel guilty, why should she be his crutch?
If he tries to ignore the rituals, he's filled with terrible fear
An inner voice screams out, TAP AGAIN
Or else he will pay very dear
It all started when his dad died from cancer – it contaminated his mind
Since then he's been tormented, solace and peace he must find
123 OCD 456 mind plays tricks 789 this life's not mine
He taps the furniture then the floor
People are staring what's that for?
He prays that one day he'll be free
123 OCD

### ANOREXIA NERVOSA

She chases a pea around her plate
Food glorious food simply fills her with hate
Her mother is sick of the daily grind
So sad that her daughter has lost her mind
She's exhausted from trying to get her to eat
She stares out the window admitting defeat
Rehab centres, weeks, months, and years
A marriage in tatters, an ocean of tears
Another counsellor with miracle cures
A course of CBT
Her sister talks till she's blue in the face
But still she can't make her see
She's knocked loudly on death's door
For the second time this year
Her mind wanders back through the past
Yet another salty tear
At 15 they thought she had it all
The whole world was there at her feet
Before the curse of mental illness
So very hard to beat
She stares at the mirror, detesting the sight
She repulsed and fat all over
We see her bones and we all feel the pain
Of Anorexia Nervosa

DSS forms! Another thorn in the side for carers! I can say in all honesty that the sight of them used to reduce me to tears. My advice is for carers to contact a benefits advisor to help with filling in the forms – it's not so frustrating.

### WELL DONE DSS

I see the postman riding his bike
He trundles along the path
I hold my breath and pray to God
That he will scurry past
But he approaches the door with the enemy
It plops loudly on the mat
That familiar large buff envelope
It's arrived and that is that
Benefit forms they fill me with dread
Long and foreboding they do in my head

Incapacity, DLA, income support, which one today?
Does he walk unaided? Does he use a stick?
Does his heart beat slow or is it quick?
Can he boil and egg? Get to the loo
How much does he rely on you?
Is he hard of hearing?
Is he blind?
Round and around my tired mind
Does he need help with preparing a meal?
Is he cheerful? depressed?
How does he feel?
Is he hard of hearing?
Does he use a frame?
By page 28 I'm going insane
Does he keep himself clean?
How's his personal care?
I'm feeling so stressed
This just isn't fair!!!!!!
The ins and outs of a nag's behind
I search for answers that I can't find
Carers need them like the plague
We try to recall but our memory's vague
I end up in tears just a blubbering mess
And it's no thanks to the DSS

# 19

# Let's Get Personal

I have written this work to explain how this condition plays havoc with the whole family not just the immediate carers. The first poem is about how my involvement as a carer would often put too much pressure on my son and it's a warning to carers especially. We become overwhelmed by our immense sadness and this can become a burden. My son has actually told me that my love became too much of a burden for him sometimes. Thank God I went for therapy myself. The family therapy sessions also helped to prise us apart, but it's taken me years to accept things …

**THE BURDEN OF LOVE**
I find your love a burden Mum I feel I must pay you back
Lying in my darkened room, it's motivation that I lack
I feel guilty about my stagnant life and I ache for things to change
Trapped within my muddled thoughts that I can't rearrange
But you can't see I'm busy or how I can't make choices
I live in two minds, not in one
Amidst many angry voices
I so much want to join life, but my unhealthy mind says no
Round and round in circles, never sure which way to go
I end up lying motionless as the months roll into years
Disrupting your life, wrecking mine
We lose count of all the tears
Yet still you stay so patient you take hold of my hand
But I find your love a burden Mum please try to understand

## IT'S NOT A MAN THING

Paul finds it very hard to express his feeling for Chris, just as Chris finds it very hard to express his feelings for his dad. The next two poems are to put into words the feelings that I know they both have for each other. Women tend to be more open with their emotions; men tend to bottle them up ...

### AS A MAN: A FATHER–SON PERSPECTIVE

As a man I find it hard to say what I feel for you inside
I've been here through your battle, so many tears I've cried
As a man I've seen your struggle, your tenacious fight to win
As a son and as a father, it's a tangled web we're in
As a man I've felt great empathy for your need to work like me
For years I've reassured you, to try to make you see
That work is not important it's your health that must come first
It's been impossible to dampen your never-ending thirst
As a man I've found it hard to cope when your life has been so sad
I've tried so hard to make you see that I'm proud to be your dad
You've walked your path with dignity, so try to understand
You've proved your worth a million times and you've proved it 'as a man'

Paul and Stephen both work in engineering; they also share a passion for football. Consequently, if the three of them go out for a pint, the conversations usually centre around work or football. It's impossible to measure the pain and frustration in Christian's case of seeing how hard his father and brother can manage to work and knowing that even six hours a week can be difficult to deal with. Pride can be a problem.

### A PROPER MAN: A SON–FATHER PERSPECTIVE

I need my dad to understand that I want to be like him
I've tried so very hard for years, but this curse won't let me win
I want my dad to understand that I try hard to find a way
To overcome the sheer fatigue I live with every day
I worry that my dad might think I'm just a lazy slob
I'd love to work like he does, in a full-time proper job
I want him to be proud of me and I hope he'll understand
That I want to be just like my dad, my dad's a proper man

You can find ways to help yourself and it doesn't matter what does it for you as long as it helps. Paul says that the colours of the flowers and plants manage to lift his spirits. He loves the springtime when he can get out there in the fresh air. No one can go through this journey and remain the same person. This poem attempts to explain the change in Paul [a wife–husband perspective].

### SCHIZOPHRENIA'S NEEDS

I watch you from the window
Gardening's helped a great deal
Like poetry has helped me through
Your garden has helped how you feel
When life has been too painful
You've found solace in the earth
Planting, weeding, sowing seeds
Then waiting for rebirth
You love the vibrant colours
They brighten up your day
They lift your flagging spirits
And help you find a way
To deal with all the sadness
That's bottled up inside
You're aware that life goes on
Despite the tears we've cried
I've seen the changes in you
You used to make me laugh
We have to find new ways
To forget the futile past
So I'll keep writing poetry
Whilst you keep planting seeds
To help us to cope with caring
And schizophrenia's needs

Another example of the difficulties we have to face is the effect on family members. My mother [who has since died] has taken this very badly. She always referred to Chris as her 'shining star'. Her hopes for his future have been shattered too.

### HER SHINING STAR: A GRANDMOTHER–GRANDSON PERSPECTIVE

My mother is almost 80, her hair is a silver sheen
Her eyes cloud over with sadness for the way things should have been
She recalls her youngest grandson – her bright and shining star
The one she pins her hopes on, the one who would go far
She'd help him with his homework, so intelligent and bright
They'd laugh and talk for hours often late at night
They shared so much together during happy carefree times
She felt so very unprepared, she should have seen the signs
Now due to modern medicine and though he's travelled far
She sees traces of her grandson, her bright and shining star

In the beginning my sister-in-law would try to get me to join the world again – this is yet another aspect of this situation. It affects the carers so much that they change into entirely different people too. We also become reclusive and isolated, in fact we take on all of the same traits as the person that we are caring for. We feel guilty if we dare to enjoy ourselves, we feel that because they can't go on holiday we shouldn't either. I can remember going to the Lake District with my sister and brother-in-law and feeling guilty the whole time. All I wanted to do was ring to find out how Chris was doing. Paul would try to stop me by saying, 'you deserve a break' and 'if you ring and he's unsettled, it will spoil your whole day'. Sometimes I would ring without him knowing. Stephen, who Chris was staying with, would also get annoyed with me and say, 'Stop phoning, he'll be OK Mum'. What was I so frightened of?

Simple: in case our going away would upset him so much that his illness would get worse and bring on a relapse. I was forever thinking about all of the things that he was missing out on. I still feel like that today even though his life has improved. My sister-in-law would try to distract me from Christian's illness, but no matter how hard she tried it was impossible.

#### BEFORE I CEASED TO BE ME

Why don't we go to the pictures this week?
I'm not in the mood I reply
You have to get out for some fun sometimes
A tear springs to my eye
I'm sorry to have to let you down
Bu he's not been well again
But you can't make him better she says
You can't miraculously stop his pain
I don't need this on top of everything else
I feel far too depressed to go
But you've been like this for ages
I've never seen you so low
Staying in won't make him get better
I'll book our seats she insists
I've told you I'm not in the mood!!!
We've never argued like this
OK I guess I can't force you to go
I feel guilty for letting her down
But I'm worried about your mental health too!!
I can picture her worried frown

I'll be OK I assure her. perhaps things will be better next week
Silence prevails for a while. She's far too upset to speak
Why is it I can't make her understand? Why is it she just can't see?
I expect her to be able to feel my pain and to know what it's like for me
She wants me to be the person she knew, happy and good company
Before fate dealt us schizophrenia
And before I ceased to be me

# 20

# A Sibling's View

Naturally Steve and Angela have been affected by Christian's illness. Stephen came to see me one day and said 'I have to talk to you about something Mum, it's about how you have become; if I said to you Angela's left me, the house has burned down and I've lost my job', you would reply "Well half the world's starving and there are people dying from cancer, and what's more your brother's got schizophrenia, life goes on Steve"' – an over-exaggeration of course, but I knew what he meant.

I'm sure there are times that he gets fed up with the work that I'm doing in mental health. He often says, 'You're either writing or you're on the phone when I come and see you.'

I would like to warn carers about how we get so used to living with this enormous problem that everything else seems very trivial, but we forget that other people's problems are still important to them. Steve says that he feels that he can't talk about his worries because he feels that we have enough to cope with as it is and that they seem so small compared to his brother's, but siblings still need their parents. Sometimes they need someone to share their worries with. There have been many times I know that I should have given him more of my time and consideration. So do try to see how difficult things can be for siblings – yes, they have a better quality of life, but it's not their fault that this has happened and getting angry is not the answer. Try to find the time and the patience to listen to their problems otherwise resentment will creep in and that can lead to family ties being broken, often forever.

### THE SON WHO WAS BORN FIRST

You were always the strongest, bigger built, robust
Nothing ever fazed you much, you've never made a fuss
You were always the easiest, steadfast, placid, kind
A more loving, gentler, happy child we'd have been hard-pushed to find
You were always logical, thoughtful, sensible too

Your sibling was more demanding with dad, with me, with you
Even now you're looking out for him, though two decades since have passed
You were there through all the bleak years that didn't go so fast
Always in the back seat, yet you've helped us through this curse
We will always count our blessings for the son who was born first


## STEPHEN'S FEELINGS

**THIS BLOODY CURSE**
It's not that I don't understand, it's not that I don't care
But sometimes I have problems which I feel that I can't share
I'm aware of my brother's pain Mum, I find it as sad as you do
But there's no room for my trivialities, so I can't confide in you
You and I used to be so close before schizophrenia knocked
But you're not the same person all these years on, to me you still seem
    shocked
You're engulfed by my brother's problems Mum, bogged down by being
    a carer
You can't see how much I miss what we had and how I wish life had been
    fairer
So try to remember I'm here Mum, I accept that my brother comes first
If only this hadn't happened and how I hate 'this bloody curse'

Recently another carer and I were talking about the difficulties we have with siblings in a group discussion. As you know schizophrenia wrecked Christian's career. Stephen however got two diplomas, an ONC and then an HNC in engineering. We never did get them framed and put on the wall. One of the professionals said, 'That isn't fair on Stephen.' Another carer said that her other son was at Uni and he got a BA. She explained that she had put the photos and scroll in the drawer out of the way for the same reasons.


## COMMENTS I HAVE HEARD FROM CARERS OVER THE YEARS

*'I feel so ill myself and then I worry what will happen to all of my family if I don't cope with my daughter's illness.'*

*'I never know how to pacify him.'*

*'What do I do when his thoughts are plaguing him?'*

*'I screamed right out loud when he said he felt like killing*

himself. I must try to stay strong!!'

'I've been arguing with her all afternoon, I can't make her see sense, she seems incapable of even understanding what I am saying to her, I feel like shaking her sometimes.'

'I'm so tired, he knows he causes it and that makes things worse.'

'We're just expected to know how to handle this confusing condition.'

'All day I've been in and out of his room begging him to get up. I sometimes think he is just plain lazy.'

'His dad is convinced that he just enjoys lying in bed and then we argue about it. Should I just leave him alone? I'm never quite sure about what I should be doing or not doing if you know what I mean.'

'It's OK for professionals, they get years of training, we're just left to get on with it and expected to cope but with absolutely no guidance at all.'

'Sometimes I feel like running away, I wonder how much more of this I can take but deep down I know I'll never do it. How would I ever be able to live with the guilt if I just abandoned them all?'

'Last night things got so bad at home that I took the car and drove down to the beach. I just sat there for about two hours. I really couldn't bear the thought of going back but eventually I did. When I got home my husband was sitting in the garden in tears and my son was in his room playing his music very loudly, he does it to drown out the voices you see. I just keep thinking that things will change but they don't ...'

'How are we expected to just understand this illness?'

'We need training sessions to help us to deal with so many things.'

'When he tells me that he is seeing things, I always say no you're not, don't be silly, but I'm never sure if I am doing the right thing because he gets angry with me and sometimes I think I make matters even worse.'

*'My husband blames me, he says I am far too soft with him and he plays on it, I end up not knowing what to think. What do you think, am I to blame?'*

*'Most of my family don't even have a clue what this is like, you have to live with it to understand, Some of them won't even talk about it, they seem embarrassed to even broach the subject but that makes me feel even worse.'*

*'No one ever offers to help us and yet I feel sure they would if this wasn't a mental illness. Why can't they see that we desperately need a break, we need support to carry on with caring.'*

*'We decided to take Christian back early. We felt that we couldn't cope for a whole weekend. At one point Paul ran down the garden, it was when Chris had yet again asked him, "Are you really my dad?" I went after him and he was standing behind the garden shed crying. He found this far too much to bear. We dropped him off at Weymarks early we just couldn't cope.'*

*'Before my son became ill he was always round my friend's house. He grew up with her kids but now they all distance themselves; it's as if we all have the bubonic plague. Sometimes he asks me why we hardly ever see them now and I don't know what to say. Well I can't say, "It's because you have a mental illness and they don't know how to cope with it", can I?'*

I was talking to a carer recently who pointed out the huge difference between his wife who suffered from cancer and his son developing schizophrenia. When his wife became ill, he had excellent support and was advised about her care every step of the way. A Macmillan nurse was provided. He said she was an angel and she had helped him in so many ways. When his son developed schizophrenia [after his wife had died], he was horrified at the difference in services. Instead of being made to feel included, informed and respected, he felt excluded, disrespected and ill-informed. He said, 'I just couldn't believe the enormous difference in the way in which I was treated as a carer to my wife as to that of being a carer to my son. With my wife I felt very included – they would talk to me about anything and everything. The support was amazing. With my son, I felt like an outcast. It was as if I had come across this wall of united silence. My question is why? They were both very ill and if anything I needed far more support with my son simply because I had lost him and his condition was so much more complex and harder to deal with. Although my wife had cancer, apart from the weight loss, she was still my wife and she was right up until she died, whereas with my son he is still here, but I am still grieving for him. The trouble is people don't understand that.

**21**

# From Both Sides

The Internet provides a whole range of websites for carers to access information. Once carers have got their heads round the situation, I suggest that they feedback any ideas that would help. We can't expect professionals to have all the answers – we are the ones living with this on a daily basis. We must also try to understand that we are not the only people that the consultant has to deal with, there are plenty more where we come from. Professionals are bogged down by bureaucracy. Carers expect them to be polite and understanding at all times, but we do not take into consideration that they might have had to deal with a very difficult situation prior to seeing us. We must all try to see things from both sides. I will now tell you about a lesson that I learned recently and that helped me to see things from an entirely different perspective.

A while ago I had a conversation with a CPN who tried to explain how difficult it is when a carer keeps asking, 'HE WILL GET BETTER THOUGH?' Professionals are often wary about giving carers false hope. I have to admit, I didn't really understand at all until recently when two carers came to see me one evening. Their 18-year-old son had become ill a few months before and as my son was nine years older, I think they wanted to know what the future had in store for them and him. They asked lots of questions, such as, 'Does your son work?', 'Has he got a girlfriend?', 'Has he got any friends?', 'Is he always tired?', etc. The mother kept saying [referring to her own son], 'he will get better though?' over and over again. It was only then that I began to appreciate what the CPN was talking about …

HE WILL GET BETTER THOUGH?
'He will get better though?' Her eyes are large and pleading
She craves my reassurance, this mother's heart is bleeding
I search my mind for answers, 'recovery is slow'
She doesn't seem to hear me, 'He will get better though?

He will get better though? This won't destroy his life?
He'll go back to work, he'll socialise, one day he'll have a wife?'
'Let's take things very slowly', I try to make things clear
'He will get better though?', she just doesn't seem to hear
'Your son's been in care for years, his condition might be worse!!
We can't just make comparisons, we're all unique and so diverse
You should have known my son, he was such a lively lad'
She searches through their happy past for the son that she once had
She's desperate to find him, the lad she's known for years
She tries hard to control herself, her eyes fill up with tears
I pat her hand to comfort her, 'recovery is slow'
But deafness hangs on in there
'He Will Get Better Though?'

**THERE IS NO MAGIC WAND**
I cannot wave a magic wand to make this go away
I'm aware of all the heartache that you go through every day
Yes I know that he's still suffering and he's plagued by angry voices
I can see that you're depleted because you don't have any choices
I know that you pray every night for a free-from-side-effects pill
Yes I know life's been like this for years but you keep on hoping still
I know he's isolated and he stays in bed all day
Sometimes I feel so helpless but I know I mustn't say
Tomorrow he'll be better and he'll leap up from his bed
So I search for reassuring words to help you with instead
Our roles through this are so diverse, yet we share this common bond
But carer try to understand, there is no magic wand

A colleague of mine who has been working in mental health for many years told me a story about something that happened to her. She was about to go on stage to do a lecture at a conference and was sitting with some carers and feeling very nervous about delivering the speech. Referring to the speaker already on stage, one of the carers said very loudly, 'What a load of bullshit, have you ever heard so much crap in all of your life?' – can you imagine how she felt? Knowing that in about five minutes time people would be saying that about her. I have met carers who are very militant and the problem is these attitudes don't get us anywhere – beating people with a stick isn't productive and neither is it fair. Let's try to understand how frustrating this is for professionals. Sometimes we expect them to provide all the answers. We must try to see that they can't and are purely there to support us.

In some areas there are training courses for carers, but it tends to be very patchy. The sessions are designed to help them by teaching them their rights, where to obtain information on housing, benefits, support, medication – the list goes on. The worrying part for me is that the early, or the bleak years as I call them, are so hard to cope with, I think it's very doubtful that many carers will find the energy to even get involved. It's hard enough coping with everyday living, let alone being able to get your head round anything else, which is why I always stress the amount of support that's needed sometimes (as in my case) for years.

Practical matters are important, but to my mind nowhere near as important as emotional support. Carers need counselling sessions to help them come to terms with their loss. I visualise carers like myself 15 years on, seeing this as all the wrong way round – by the time we've come to terms, we've already learned most of the practical parts along the way. In short, get the support right at the start and only then will carers be able to attend classes to learn more. I'm not saying that it's possible to stop a carer's grief, but we can try to find ways to help them cope with it.

At this stage I must write about the mistakes that I too often make. I'm sure when professionals read this book they would feel both hurt and angry if I didn't have the humility to admit that I often lose my way. It's not all one-way traffic. I'm aware that I have made mistakes that have made their role harder. An example is in the poem, 'Desperate Phone Calls'. When Chris was in Weymarks, he would ring me time after time. Some days I could cope better than others. The staff would say, 'When he starts getting angry, put the phone down, but before you do tell him to go and talk to one of the staff and we will sort him out.' Although I'd moan about it, I still felt unable to put the phone down and I am now able to see how frustrating this was for the staff.

If you were to ask how long it takes to mend a broken leg, the answer would be easy to find, but considering the brain has more neurological connections than the entire telephone system of planet earth, it's hardly surprising that a CPN can't say, 'Give it a few months and then he/she will be fine'. If I had £1 for every time I've asked, 'When will he be better?' I'd be well off. It takes carers a long time to realise this. We want to know how much longer we have to witness their pain because we know the end of their pain is the only thing that will stop ours. Patience and understanding are imperative but it has to come from both sides.

This particular week turned out to be worse than most. Firstly,

Chris received a letter informing him that he wouldn't be offered a job after all. Secondly, a psychiatrist took it upon himself to say publicly, 'Let's hear about all the terrible things your son has done' whilst I was conducting a presentation and thirdly, I had problems explaining to the DSS that my son should never have had his DLA stopped. The first incident affected Christian's mental health very badly. In all the time he has been on clozapine, he has never complained of voices or hallucinations, but it all came flooding back. He asked us to remove all of his tablets and knives from his flat saying that they scared him. He said his lower arms felt pumped up and that he could see silver flashes on the left on many occasions. We rang Weymarks and they patiently talked him through his fears; we also rang social services and they helped too.

At one stage we were scared he would relapse. He had to be so strong. After a few weeks he did his first day at a voluntary job, but came home early saying that he'd been seeing things and was feeling very unwell. I think we were all feeling tense due to the stress of that particular week and Chris picks things up and consequently gets affected by the situation. Following many frantic phone calls, he was given some tranquillisers to try to help him get through this bad patch. As you can see, you have to look at what is going on to see why a patient's mental health is deteriorating and this particular week is a prime example of the effects that situations can have, but also remember that sometimes there will not be a reason – it can just happen and the only explanation is the fact that they suffer from schizophrenia – end of story.

Carers and professionals can work well together. We need to be committed enough to put aside our own feelings. If we feel we are being criticised, we must be humble enough to admit that we may be doing something wrong. And therefore rethink our own behaviour.

## MOVING ON – WEDNESDAY 16TH APRIL, 2009

An update on how the 'other mind' therapy continues to help all of us.

On Easter Sunday we all went to Hyde Hall Gardens. We took a picnic and after walking round, we sat down to eat. Chris had been fine all day, but suddenly he changed and became anxious and frustrated. Denise, his personal assistant, tried to talk to him about what was suddenly bothering him.

He said, 'Don't try to talk to me because I am in the "other mind"'. After about 15 minutes he explained to all of us what it was like. He said, 'It wasn't just me being difficult, it was as if I'd been taken over and I wasn't even able to explain myself but I can see it all very clearly now. At the time it's really difficult and it sort of sucks me in, then it passes but it takes time.'

Once upon a time this incident would have led to frustration, anger, arguments, all-round high expressed emotion. Within 15 minutes everything was fine and we all moved on.

The NICE guidelines state that ten weeks of CBT is adequate therapy. I wrote earlier about how CBT purely worsened Christian's symptoms. I'm not saying it's not useful – it does have its place, I'm sure it works very well for mild anxiety/depression. Recently I was attending a conference in London and they were talking about CBT online and how you can turn on your PC and receive a course of CBT. The demonstrator went on to say that the best part about it is that you don't have to go out of the house. I asked him had he ever been clinically depressed and he replied, 'No'. I said, 'Well I have and the last thing I would have been able to do is sit in front of a TV screen and, more to the point, isn't recovery about social inclusion and getting people out of the house?' In the end we had to agree to disagree.

## UNDERACHIEVING

Christian has always wanted to work. He'd been managing a part-time job in a warehouse since moving into his flat, but after about a year he was made redundant. Yet again far too much time on his hands became a problem. His social worker didn't help – she seemed to think that we were pushing him into working again. During the spell of almost a year, I could see his condition deteriorating and he was becoming more and more depressed. He'd stare out of the window for long periods. It was all going on out there but Christian wasn't a part of any of it. Yet again nothingness …

I made an appointment with the chief executive of our local NHS Trust who listened to me and said he felt, as I did, that the social worker was not helping Chris find anything that would give him a sense of achievement. The chief executive offered Chris a job doing some admin work at Thurrock Hospital, which is almost opposite where we live. This has been very successful and he still works there today. It's all about normalising things, and Chris being able to say, 'I go to work' helps with his self-esteem. The ladies he works with are very supportive – some of them have even read my books to help them to understand.

I was asked by a lecturer at the Institute of Psychiatry recently to read a poem to some students entitled, 'The Ambulance Down in the Valley'. Amazingly, it was written in 1895 – 114 years ago! It's all about how these people keep falling off the edge of a cliff, but instead of putting a fence around the top to protect them, they have put an ambulance down in the valley, and sadly we're still not getting it right, but at least personalisation of Direct Payments and individual budgets are a step in the right direction. Relapse prevention is the answer.

# 22

# What are Direct Payments?

Direct Payments is the name given to the means by which public bodies can give people money with which to arrange to meet the needs for which support or services would otherwise have been provided to them. At present they are only generally available from local councils in relation to their responsibility to meet 'social care' needs, but they are also being piloted in health as part of the Personal Health Budget Pilot, and across a number of other areas (such as Access to Work and Supporting People) in nine 'Right to Control Trailblazer' areas.

Local councils should be informing everyone assessed as needing 'social care' support about Direct Payments, and, with some rare exceptions, have a duty to make them available to every person who is 'willing and able (alone or with assistance)' to manage them. Since November 2009, this includes people accepted by the council as 'suitable' to manage Direct Payments wholly on behalf of someone who has been judged to 'lack capacity' to agree to Direct Payments.

Direct Payments were introduced in 1997 as a direct result of campaigning by disabled people and their allies. Whilst they have not always been made as readily available or with the degree of flexibility that they should have, they have proved a highly successful way of enabling people to take greater control, both of their care and support arrangements, and over their lives. They can and do work as well for people who use mental health services as they can for anyone else.

For a number of years, there have been continued attempts to promote the use of Direct Payments within mental health services, which are provided jointly by local councils and the NHS. In 1996 the DH published *Direct Payments for People with Mental Health Problems: A guide to action,* and the National Social Inclusion Programme published a companion guide for people who use mental health services and for carers: *An Introduction to Direct Payments in Mental Health Services: Information for people eligible to use mental health services and carers.*[1]

Since these were written, Personal Budgets have begun (but only very slowly) to be introduced into mental health services, and the exclusions relating to people on certain sections of the Mental Health Act have been lifted. These changes are outlined in the DH *Summary of Changes to Direct Payments*.[2]

The level and type of support a person will receive, and the amount of control and choice they have in shaping that support, is changing, but the duty to make Direct Payments available is not changing. They can be received as a way of meeting some or all of a person's needs under traditional 'community care' arrangements, which are gradually being replaced by Personal Budgets, or as a way of using all or part of a Personal Budget.

However, despite the length of time they have been established, and the large amount of evidence as to their effectiveness, many people using mental health services have never been informed about Direct Payments or offered them, and even where many have, they have found the application process hostile, protracted and confusing, or their applications declared 'ineligible' by funding panels. This reflects a deeper problem in a mental health system which still operates very much on traditional assumptions and methods and has not yet adapted to the requirements of providing support and services which are based on the contemporary principles and values outlined so clearly in *Putting People First* (DH, 2007).[3]

That change will come is demonstrated by two new publications, *Paths to Personalisation* (NMHDU, 2010)[4] and *Personalisation in Mental Health* (CWR, 2010)[5] but in the meantime it is important that people are prepared for the obstacles which may arise.

Every local council will publish its own guide to Direct Payments. Some publish a version for people using mental health services which takes account of the different structures and terminology of mental health services. A fair number of these guides have not been updated to reflect the changes introduced in November 2009, which removed the previous exclusions relating to sections of the

1. http://www.socialinclusion.org.uk/publications/Direct_Payments_SU_Guide.pdf
2. http://www.dh.gov.uk/en/Publicationsandstatistics/Publications/Publications PolicyAndGuidance/DH_107271
3. http://www.idea.gov.uk/idk/aio/14007769
4. www.pathstopersonalisation.org.uk (this website contains a number of examples of how Direct Payments are being used)
5. http://www.centreforwelfarereform.org.uk

Mental Health Act and some other mental health legislation.

The Department of Health has produced an updated guide to Direct Payments (*A Guide to Receiving Direct Payments from Your Local Council: A route to independent living*, DH, September 2009)[6] which, whilst not being specific to mental health services, includes the following information.

### DIRECT PAYMENTS FOR PEOPLE UNDER MENTAL HEALTH LAW

- From November 2009 people who are under mental health law will also be able to get Direct Payments.

- In some specific cases the council may decide that the conditions placed on someone by mental health law may make it more difficult for Direct Payments to be used to meet his or her needs. However, in all other cases, being placed under mental health law should not stop you getting Direct Payments if you want them.

### HOW DO DIRECT PAYMENTS WORK?

- The vast majority of people who are assessed as needing services have a right to Direct Payments. Equally, you should not be pressured into having Direct Payments if you prefer services to be arranged by the council.

- Your council will tell you more about the arrangements and the limited circumstances in which Direct Payments are not appropriate.

- Having read this guide, you may still have many questions about Direct Payments. Do not worry. You should not feel that you are the only person asking these questions, and you may receive help from someone else with managing Direct Payments if you need it. Most local councils have established support services for people wishing to use Direct Payment schemes. They will be able to tell you about services in your area.

---

6. http://www.dh.gov.uk/en/publicationsandstatistics/publications/publications policyandguidance/dh_083561

- Many people considering Direct Payments for the first time find it helpful to talk to people with experience of using Direct Payments. Your local council or support scheme should be able to put you in touch with other Direct Payment users.

Your care co-ordinator should be able to give you information about how Direct Payments can be accessed in your local area.

If you have difficulty in obtaining information, or if you would like a copy of a DVD showing the difference that Direct Payments can make, please contact: Robin Murray care of spotlightonschizo phrenia@yahoo.co.uk or ring 07747 536067 and leave a message with your request and contact details.

### CHRISTIAN, DIRECT PAYMENTS AND HIS PERSONAL ASSISTANT

Christian has been receiving Direct Payments for about five years now, and during that time he's employed five personal assistants. His current PA, Denise Claxton, has made an enormous difference to his life and ours.

Before we talk about the benefits of Direct Payments, a word of warning. We followed the procedure and Christian was assessed by an occupational therapist who could see that his need was to socialise more and so he was duly accepted. We advertised for a PA in our local job centre. Chris and I interviewed five people and he decided he had the most in common with a young man of 25. He worked with Chris for 14 months before we found to our horror, that he had embezzled £380 from Christian's bank account. He'd taken him shopping at Lakeside and when Chris said he needed to go to the toilet, he said 'Let me look after your wallet', etc. During that few minutes, he drew the money from the ATM machine. Luckily the cameras were working and the police brought the film round to show us exactly how he did it. Up until we actually saw him on camera stealing the money, Paul refused to believe that he'd done it. This young man did not have a criminal record; this was his first offence. The worst part for me was that he knew what Chris had been through [and was still going through]. He was taken to court and received 200 hours community service and a £200 fine.

Now to talk about the difference a good PA can make to someone's life.

As you know isolation has been a huge problem for Christian, but these days life is very different. Denise has put together two scrapbooks and they visually show the enormous difference Direct Payments have made. She has taken photos on days out and kept programmes from the many shows they have seen together. She is also helping Chris with very practical tasks.

Our local NHS Trust are using the scrapbooks and the many notes she has made about how to be a good PA, to train their support workers. Looking at the books, it's easy to see how Christian's life has opened up and improved. It's hard to describe what it feels like when he calls me to say, 'Mum I'm in London and we're having a meal before we go to the theatre'. Chris has done more in the past two years than he did in the 18 years leading up to him accessing Direct Payments.

So let's take a look at the benefits from all of our perspectives.

## DIRECT PAYMENTS: 'A KEY TO SOCIAL INCLUSION AND MENTAL WELL-BEING'

During this journey the thing that has struck me the most is the lack of facilities for these young people to help them to recover.

All we can say is thank God we heard about Direct Payments. Distraction from symptoms makes life so much easier to deal with; without a quality of life there is little else but the symptoms to focus on.

Recently I presented a keynote speech to 300 pharmacists at the UKPPG (UK Psychiatric Pharmacy Group) conference in Leicester. The speech lasted for 50 minutes and Christian came with us. He decided to sit outside while I talked about the early years of his journey – the last thing he needs is any reminders of the early years. At the end we watched the DVD of the documentary made for the BBC and Paul went out of the room to bring Chris in. As he entered the room everyone in the audience stood up and applauded him. He had no idea that they were applauding him until I told him. This act of respect made up for the stigma that has hurt him in the past. Respect is the very least that people deserve. Then he went up to the podium and read 'New Choices' and there was even more applause.

This next poem has been written from the service users' perspective. At last people are being given ...

NEW CHOICES

For two long decades I've had no choices
Just years of social exclusion
Nowhere to go, nothing to do
Normality? It was just an illusion
A pat on the head and there you go son
Sit all day at the drop-in at MIND
Drugged up to the eyeballs with a liquid cosh
Life simply passing me by
I had no choice I shut up, I put up
Lost every ounce of motivation
Life became a living hell
Borne out of my deep frustration
Relapse was inevitable, back on the wards
Through that ever-revolving door
Days spent in bed – medication-isolation
Wondering endlessly what's this life for?
My lost life was screaming out for change
All hope was fading fast
Then finally a miracle – NEW CHOICES at long last
Personalisation means so many choices
At last they can hear our desperate voices
Individual budgets the vital key
A far better life for you and me
Enhancing the new life I now have to live
Now I feel I have much more to give
A reason to get out of bed each day
Our needs all differ but that's OK
NEW CHOICES – FLEXIBILITY
Places to go and people to see
Relapse prevention, new choices for all
Protecting us from each painful fall
There's no more need to keep raising our voices
The future is bright – we've been given NEW CHOICES

What saddens me more than anything is that there are so many carers who don't even know about Direct Payments and whose lives, like ours, would improve. I also sympathise with the professionals who I have met recently who desperately want to help but need more time and indeed training to deal with accessing Direct Payments. We feel relieved simply because we didn't allow the painful incident of the theft to deter us from carrying on with this scheme. Had we given up, we would never have witnessed the benefits and Chris could have relapsed again due to having no quality of life.

## 'MY PERSPECTIVE'
## by DENISE CLAXTON [PA TO CHRISTIAN]

Firstly, I would like to thank Christian and his family for welcoming me into their lives so that I could help support him and them through the rest of his journey and help him manage and enjoy everyday living by giving him encouragement and motivation, and showing him basic practical skills.

I try to get him to see that life should be fun, most of the time. I always say that you should live for the moment and not worry too much about what's around the corner. I encourage him to eat healthily, exercise, keep diaries and use calendars, read, watch television and learn about the world we live in. I feel it has been very beneficial for him to be out and about instead of the days when he had nothing to do.

Thankfully Direct Payments was a way of opening up his world, even though he had a struggle finding someone who was compatible with him, he is now slowly finding his feet.

Christian seems happy and confident and in his own words, experiencing something he has longed for and that is seeing things and doing things he wouldn't have been able to cope with before having a personal assistant.

He is far more relaxed and positive, he smokes less and is much more domesticated, but he is still improving on a day-to-day basis. I chose this job because I wanted to try something different [my trade is hairdressing]. I am a carer myself with two children with disabilities. My oldest [a daughter aged 18] has severe ADHD and kidney problems and the younger one has kidney and bladder problems; also my mother and sister are coping with their own mental health problems and I have always felt a need to give something back. I will continue to work alongside Christian however long it takes. I try to get him to interact socially by introducing him to people in public places, such as a café or park or even whilst we are on a shopping trip, using my own judgement of character. This has been both successful and rewarding for him.

I've had to learn to deal with the unreality of Christian's paranoia, for instance when we first met, he would think that people knew what he was thinking or he would hear something coming from the noise of the radio or the wheels of a car. I would say, 'Is it really possible to hear a voice actually talking to you from the radio Chris?' Gradually he realised that it was just in his head – an unreal thought or TOM [the 'other mind'] as he calls it.

Nowadays, when he gets a negative thought, he understands almost straightaway that he was not focusing properly. We have had some amazing days over a two-year period and I can see an incredible change in Christian's life. Personally I think in time Christian will learn and mature and be capable of talking and encouraging other people who suffer from schizophrenia.

# 23

# Recovery or Discovery?

It's just as if Chris is awakening to the world around him, a very different world from the one he's lived in for all these years. He's waking up simply because his symptoms are nowhere near as severe these days – why? His quality of life is so much better and he's distracted from at least some of the crap that goes on in his head.

Below is a list of the things which we feel have all gone towards Christian's recovery. The list is in no particular order, although I do believe that first and foremost is definitely LOVE!

1. Love and support from his family
2. The right medication
3. Talking therapies and art therapy
4. Veg EPA omega-3 fatty acids
5. Family therapy
6. Support from professionals
7. Our pets – African grey parrot and our border terrier [we've had four dogs during Christian's illness]
8. A hot tub [for relaxation]
9. Attention to diet
10. Part-time paid employment
11. Supported housing
12. Physical exercise
13. A befriender
14. Direct Payments
15. The right personal assistant
16. Carer therapy [for me]

The biggest lesson for me during the past 20 years is about quality of life. I call this journey 'A Journey of Discovery, Opportunities, Achievements and Hope'.

- Discovery? Because we have to discover what to take on and what to avoid, what helps and, of course, what hinders recovery.

- Opportunities? We need opportunities, e.g., to work voluntarily, part time, whatever suits – something to get up out of bed for.

- Achievements? The awards that Chris has received and making the film, 'Loving Christian' [all of these are his own achievements] have helped him. In 2004 Chris received a local award for how he's coped in the face of adversity and for finding the courage to appear on National TV and say, 'Take a look, this is me, but look beyond the label of schizophrenia and learn that we're not all axe-wielding maniacs'. Chris was presented with The Majors Award, part of the Thurrock Civic Awards. We attended the ceremony, along with over 400 people. He was asked to go onto the stage where he read a speech and the next poem. He left the stage to a standing ovation. To say that we felt proud would be an understatement!

- Hope? We have always encouraged him, talked to him about his own self-worth, lifted his flagging spirits to help improve his self-confidence. I always tell him 'Remember you're as good as the next man and better than most.'

There is far more to recovery than mind-numbing medication. We can't expect people to stay well without feeding the spirit. Recovery is about having choices. These days he does have choices and not just a pat on the head and 'There you go mate, you can always go and sit down MIND Day Centre all day long. What more could you possibly ask for?'

I would like to see far more uptake of Direct Payments and individual budgets. There should be far more training around Direct Payments for service users, carers, professionals and more importantly, personal assistants. Paul, Chris, myself and Denise recently took part in a film for CSIP (Care Service Improvement Partnership) which will promote Direct Payments nationally.

Christian lives independently, works part time, both paid and voluntarily, he employs a PA and is engaged in an English course at college. In our wildest dreams we would never have thought it possible. I'm often asked, 'Has he got a girlfriend?' Well who knows what's around the corner? Maybe it will be the subject of my next book!

# 24

# Back Where We Belong

For 32 years my sister-in-law Marilyn was my closest friend. We met when we were 16 and Paul was best man to his older brother Peter and Peter was best man at our wedding. Our children were brought up together. I had Stephen, and a few months later she had Paul. I had Christian, again a few months later she had Maxine. She was there holding my hand when Chris was born at home. We lived opposite each other as the children were growing up. Paul and Peter ran a butcher's shop together for ten years.

To cut a long story short the differences in our lives were too vast for any of us to cope with and our family fell apart.

When Christian became ill she didn't know how to comfort me – the truth is no one on this earth could have comforted me. When Chris started to show signs of schizophrenia she was enjoying her first grandchild. When Maxine got married, Chris had relapsed and was in care. Paul and Peter have suffered immensely too.

Over the years Marilyn and I had always talked about Maxine's wedding day [her being the only girl] and how we would shop for our outfits together and how I would help her with the wedding plans. Chris was 25, in care and still very ill. I don't even know how I made it to the wedding. I can remember telling Maxine how sorry I was for not being there for her on her special day, to which she replied, 'I understand, don't worry.'

On May 3rd 2009 as usual I was up early writing this book. It was almost finished, but unbeknown to me, there was to be a final chapter. Despite living very close to each other I've only seen her in the car a few times during the past 11 years. I was putting Alfie back in the car after a walk and she pulled up in her car right next to me. We talked and she explained her hurt too. It's been very emotional, many tears have been shed, but I have no doubts about our future together.

Paul believes that we were meant to go our separate ways

because our pain would have spoilt their joy, such happy times watching their grandchildren growing up was never meant to be subjected to our pain. This is why I urge carers to join a carers' group [even though I left it years]. I can see now that being with people who are experiencing the same hurt is supportive and it strengthens you. Over a decade on and we all feel able to cope with this. We now feel that we were destined to take this journey alone. What I find so amazing is the timing of this reunion, because I am rewriting this book and us getting back together has enabled me to write about how the weight of this condition was far too heavy for any of us to cope with as a warning to other carers.

They say we take things out on those who are closest to us; that's what I did. I wanted to transfer my feelings onto her so that she would be there for me 24/7. I didn't think about her life or how this was affecting her. I didn't see how much I had changed either. So carers yet another word of warning – talk openly to those you care for, try to help them to understand in order to avoid losing precious time together.

Schizophrenia managed to destroy our relationship, and I've written this poem for Marilyn ...

**BACK WHERE WE BELONG**

A decade passed,ten wasted years since we shared happy times
Disaster struck, it hurt us all, our lives went out of rhyme
It chewed us up, then spat us out, we needed desperately to talk
But schizophrenia's hard to understand, you have to walk the walk
It wrecks long-term relationships no matter who they're with
We were totally depleted, we had nothing left to give
We must look to the future, forget those wasted, lonely years
We must all forgive each other, it's time for smiles, not tears
Yesterday is gone and tomorrow's a brand new day
No one is to blame, so there's nothing more to say
We can all see things so clearly, for each other we'll be strong
Let's look forward to the future now we're 'back where we belong'

Words are a great comfort and the words that sum everything up for me are in the Serenity Prayer:

*God grant us the serenity to accept the things we cannot change, The courage to change the things we can And the wisdom to know the difference.*

A CARER*

I care about hope, respect and meaning
Not labels that define, confine then consign
I care about trust – the real foundation of your work
Not suspicion that clouds our thoughts and breeds paranoia
Nor fear that limits our imagination and destroys our dreams

I care about power and how it's used
The power of understanding, believing and being with
Not the power of ignoring, excluding and controlling
'The needle and the damage done' – they say it feels like rape

I care about the good ones – they know who they are
The ones who've been there – in terror – in despair
The ones who've walked the long hard road
And still go back sometimes
The ones who listen and learn and show they care
The ones who dare to stop and think
Is this good enough for my mum, my son?
The ones who know it could be me, it could be mine
This week, this year, any time
How to keep them there – to shine a light for all?

So if you care about these things
Are you not a carer too?

Christian's social worker has just applied for Direct Payments for me and Paul to take quarterly four-day breaks, recharging our batteries will help us to cope with caring.

And so our journey comes to an end. Firstly I'd like to thank Christian, whose courage has provided my determination to write this book and for having the strength to deal with schizophrenia. Paul, Stephen, Angela and the rest of my family for their love and support. Denise Claxton for her determination to give Christian a better quality of life. Matthew for his friendship, support, and advice. Robin Murray-Neill, the most talented person I've ever met. Thanks to my friends – [you all know who you are.Thanks to Dr Dianne Lefevre; Gwen Simpson [art therapist]; Marie Lyn Bannis [Christian's

---

* Poem by Jen Kilyon, another carer and co-author (with Theresa Smith) of *A Straight Talking Introduction to Caring for Someone with Mental Health Problems.* PCCS Books, 2009.

current social worker / key worker] has done a great job in supporting us all; Francis Griffiths, group analyst; and Kathy Swearingen, family therapist. Thanks to Marilyn, for understanding and helping all of us to build bridges. And last but not least special thanks to my dearest sister Christine, who died on December 4th 2009 following a very long illness but was always there for me.

WHO WE ARE

Schizophrenia can be a teacher
It's made us who we are
Two decades on and now you're 35
We were shell-shocked, we were grieving
We marvelled at your strength
An iron will that's helped you to survive
We're aware that you're a different son
Nothing like the son we knew
The son that we brought up for 15 years
But this was to be our destiny
We could not intervene
We waded through a river made from tears
Schizophrenia can be a teacher
It's taught us all so much
Compassion, kindness and humility
Every one of us has changed
As this journey took its course
It's made us all how we were meant to be
You say 'I don't achieve much Mum
I'd have a loved a wife and kids
In the workplace I haven't fared so well'
I remind you of your strength, your sheer tenacity
How you've managed to survive this living hell
So don't question things you've missed
Reflect on what you've learned
On this journey that has taken us so far
Let's look forwards to the future
Be aware of what we've gained
This has made us all exactly who we are

# Afterword

---

## 5ᵀᴴ JANUARY, 2010

A carer rang me yesterday. She had read an article I'd written for a magazine and wanted to talk about her 27-year-old son. He [like many others] had become ill at university four years previously. I asked her if she knew about Direct Payments and the answer yet again was no. She explained that she was a widow and that she was finding it so hard to cope. How many more carers are totally unaware that Direct Payments even exist?

*Carers: ask about Direct Payments – you deserve it!*